Caveman Bodies in a Corporate Jungle:

How to stay healthy while excelling in a work environment

Dr. John Barrett

TAWC Publishing

Los Angeles

Library of Congress Cataloging-in-Publication Data
Barrett, John
Caveman Bodies in a Corporate Jungle: How to stay healthy while excelling
in a work environment / John Barrett – First edition
ISBN-10 0-998782319 ISBN-13 978-0-9987823-1-7 LCCN 2017909541
Includes bibliographic references
1. Work-life Balance. 2. Stress-management (Psychology). 3. Self-
motivation (Psychology). 4. Mindfulness. 5. Positive-thinking
I. Title. II. Title: How to stay healthy while excelling in a work
environment.
650.01-dc22

PUBLISHER'S NOTE:

For more information about Dr. John Barrett see his blog and website at
www.DrJohnBarrett.com

You cannot buy your youth; you can only preserve it.

Contents

Have we really come that far? Between monstrous traffic, life shattering layoffs, and threatening deadlines, our work life can seem like a jungle. Why do we pay money to pick fresh fruit or get into the wilderness? With a little effort, we can have the best of both worlds.

Who are we? Where do humans come from? Are we made for today's work life? By looking at our success factors that helped us evolve, we can learn how to adapt and succeed in any environment.

What do you need to
know about your
current work
environment to
succeed? Early humans
learned all they could
about their landscape,
flora, and fauna in order
to adapt and survive.
Drastic changes could
happen overnight.

Learn what you need to know about your work environment to survive
and strategize your success despite the constant threat of change.

Your central nervous system is like a
central processing unit of a
computer. It basically controls all of
your bodily functions from health
maintenance to emergency reactions
for survival. Learn how it works and
take control of your health and ability
to succeed. Learn to stay calm,
focused, and productive with good
health.

We react 20 time stronger to emotional stimuli than we do to intellectual facts. Overreacting to a bunch of small emotions can create lots of anxiety and lead to poor health

and low productivity. This can rob us of our opportunities to excel and succeed in life. Learn how to resolve emotions and stay present and focused. Learn to enjoy life with success and happiness.

Do you have enough quiet time in your life? Learn to nourish body, mind, and spirit. Give yourself a bręak while awakening your higher self with activities that you are passionate about. Learn how to meditate and make time for hobbies. Learn the benefits of daily quiet time and living with spiritual nourishment. Learn how laughter and adding enjoyment to your life can help you stay healthy and succeed.

One of the best ways to manage stress is through a regulated diet. Learn how the right diet can help increase your focus, productivity, and threshold for stress. The right diet will strengthen your immune system, increase your health, and ability to succeed

Live without the drama. Stay calm, focused, and present. Live with good health, be more productive, and excel in all your endeavors. Develop your intuition and creativity. Express your passion. Do all this while deepening relationships with friends, family, and colleagues. Learn to conquer stress and live with more peace, harmony, and abundance.

Time is one resource that can never be replaced. Learn how to use it wisely to achieve your goals. Learn how to identify your critical success factors. Learn how to manage tasks based on urgency and importance. Develop good time management habits and add to your success, health, and happiness.

Nobody is an island unto themselves. At work, we can achieve much more as a team. Teamwork requires communication. Everybody is different and may communicate in different fashions. Learn the best form of communication for the points you wish to share with your team. Learn the benefits of the spoken word vs. email. Learn how to communicate and encourage coworkers to work with you and discourage misunderstandings and people who may work against you.

An organized work space helps to maintain focus and productivity. Learn how to arrange your space to accommodate efficiency. Analyze your daily work flow processes and set up your space to mirror them. Once organized, add some  traditional feng shui principals to your office and see their benefits. Learn to add some tradition to your modern condition for an enhanced performance oriented environment.

 Your cognitive skills and level of genius are forever fluctuating. Learn how you can strengthen both. Learn how to leverage both to assist in your success and maintenance of optimal health. You may even have a big *aha moment* that sets you ahead of the pack for life.

Have you ever thought of cultivating your passion? Discover what your passion is. Learn to cultivate your passion and watch your zest for life blossom like never before. Watch new opportunities come your way. Learn to express who you really are. Begin living your life with the magic of passion.

14. Skill 6—Adapting to Change and Managing Yourself   173

Research shows that humans evolved and outlived many other species due to our ability to adapt to change. Be prepared for change by looking ahead. Do research on your career to make sure you will not be made obsolete by technological changes. Do financial projections to make sure you will have enough resources to meet your needs. Make sure you have enough comforts in life to make your down time nourishing. Learn to stay ahead of the game so you can adapt to change in a timely manner. Don't be caught off guard due to poor planning.

15. Skill 7—Maintaining a Positive and Winning Attitude   183

Newton's law of motion says for every action there is a reaction. The ancient Hindu concept of karma says this applies to our thoughts and attitude as well. Learn how a positive and winning attitude

will help create and maintain positive situations in your life. Learn how a positive attitude will keep your cognitive skills and central nervous system in optimal performance. Learn how to develop and maintain a positive and winning attitude to overcome adversity and maintain optimal health while excelling in life.

Acknowledgments

I wish to thank my nephew, Robert Dudley, PhD, for his wisdom and guidance as a developmental editor. I wish to thank my friends, Dan Barresi, Rich Curtin, and George Avants—all well-seasoned corporate professionals—for their generous contributions as beta-readers. I wish to thank my brother George Barrett, MD, for his medical review. I wish to thank my friend, a world renowned and award-winning artist, Tony Deluz, for his creative illustrations and cover design. I would like to thank my copy editor, Keri Schreiner, for her depth of skills in polishing the text while preserving my personal voice and tone. Finally, I am grateful for the opportunity both to have lived such a rich and diverse life and to share the knowledge and wisdom I have gained within these pages.

About the Author and the Book

Most stress factors and health problems in the corporate environment stem from the fact that our bodies have evolved to survive in a different environment. Over the last 100,000 years, our environment and culture has changed dramatically. However, our bodies have not. Our bodies and everything about us have evolved to master living in a *jungle*. However, most of us have never seen a jungle. Instead of running, hunting, and gathering, many of us work in corporate environments that require a different set of skills. These skills may not come naturally. Our body, mind, and spirit may crave the diverse activities and exposure to nature for which we have naturally evolved. Our constant exposure to the unnatural corporate environment not only deprives our bodies of their natural habitat, it can lead to high levels of stress, frustration, job dissatisfaction, and poor health. At this point, the corporate environment may seem like a *jungle*. However, it does not have to be that way.

The purpose of this book is to help you understand how to stay healthy and lead a happy, successful, and prosperous life while excelling in today's corporate environment. This book is a culmination of my personal and professional life experiences. As a former CPA, I worked for Deloitte & Touche in Boston, Sydney, London, and Los Angeles. Overall, I spent 20 years auditing and consulting for Fortune 500 corporations, as well as for many smaller, privately owned companies. However, after reading Steven Covey's book, *First Things First*, I realized I was not on my path. I then participated in a program on guidance through synchronicity. This led me to answer a calling to practice medicine in 1997. After graduating from Emperor's College of Traditional Oriental Medicine in Santa Monica, California in 2001, I went to China and completed a post-graduate externship at the University of Beijing Teaching Hospital. Since returning in 2002, I have established a private practice in the Century City Medical Plaza in Los Angeles, where I also serve on staff at Cedars Sinai Medical Center.

With 20 years' firsthand working knowledge of corporate environments and the cultures, systems, and infrastructures that support them, I have developed an expertise in this arena. Additionally, with 5 years of medical studies and research, plus having diagnosed and treated thousands of patients in my 15 years of private practice, I have also developed an expertise in medicine and human health. Given this dual expertise, I am well aware of the stress factors of the corporate environment and how they may adversely affect your health and performance. I also have a keen understanding of what you can do about it and the restrictions you must deal with.

From my exposure as a healthcare practitioner, it is clear that we humans are novices when it comes to mastering the corporate environment. Too many people fail, burn out, live unhappily, or unnecessarily suffer with poor health. This is evidenced by the soaring costs of healthcare, sick pay, and disability payouts. My dual expertise has thus fueled a new calling in life: rather than simply treat illnesses, I feel compelled to combine my knowledge and my experiences to improve both health and corporate life.

In *Caveman Bodies in a Corporate Jungle*, I offer a brief overview of human evolution and health, followed by a discussion of the primary stress factors in a corporate environment and how they can inhibit the ability of your central nervous system (CNS) to maintain health. I then explain how to de-stress and the key role of diet in stress management and in optimizing health, energy, and focus. Further, I explain how to develop basic skills needed in addition to good health to survive and succeed in the corporate jungle. These skills include time management, communication, logistical design of workspace, mental acuity, cultivating passion, managing your life, and maintaining a positive, winning attitude.

It is my intention to help you form a vision of what's possible and to develop the skills and best practices necessary to make your corporate experience natural, successful, and happy, with the added rewards of excellent health, prosperity, and longevity. You can read this book cover to cover or simply focus on those areas you find most relevant to your current environment, health, and skill sets. If you find this book enlightening, please feel free to pass the word by writing a positive review on the site where you purchased it. Thank you and enjoy!

Part 1

The Caveman and the Jungle

CHAPTER 1

Drama of the Day in a Corporate Jungle

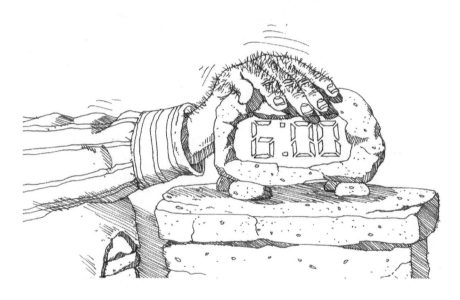

You wake to an alarm. You need your sleep, so the alarm is set at the last possible minute necessary to get you to work on time. You rush into the shower and barely say good morning to your teenage daughter, who is failing school because of boyfriend problems. You don't talk to your spouse, because he or she left an hour ago. You don't have time to eat anything, besides there is nothing good to eat because no one had time to shop. You jump in your car only to hit traffic on the freeway, which will cause you to be late for your first meeting. While you call ahead on your cell phone to give the office a heads up, someone decides to totally cut you off causing a near-death experience.

You arrive at work and immediately jump into your meeting with your mind racing and unfocused. During the meeting, you are informed that your department is going to be restructured and layoffs are possible. After the meeting, you rush to your office only to discover that your to-do list has expanded by 250% over night. To take your mind off things, you decide to check the stock market and learn that your 401k retirement strategy is not working. At this point, you suddenly feel like you are starving and rush down to the cafeteria to grab a muffin and a cup of coffee. You know that you are not supposed to eat the muffin because you are overweight with high cholesterol and muffins are on the bad list. You decide to get it anyway because things are so bad, you need a little treat. Besides, you can start the dieting tomorrow when you have a clearer perspective.

After returning to your desk, you get a phone call from your spouse informing you that your daughter was caught skipping class yet again and may be expelled from school. Your spouse is totally fed up with working and being a full-time parent, and informs you that you need to pick up the slack. You don't know what to do and feel like screaming. Everyone at work thinks you are a grump and you don't care. After all, you get the work done no matter what it takes.

At this point, the idea of running through a jungle to hunt down a wild boar and gather fresh fruit for an afternoon barbeque back at the cave sounds like a great idea. After all, that is what your body is engineered for. However, by today's standards this is what we call a planned, leisurely day off and, by the way things are going at work, you may not get one anytime soon.

Does any of this sound familiar? I am not suggesting we should go back to being hunter-gatherers, as I could write a similar satire for that life-style. Think of all the modern conveniences we do have, such as warm beds, electricity, and buttons to push for everything from food to transportation and much of our entertainment. In addition, we are very rarely confronted with life-threatening events. Instead of going back in time, we need to find a balance that gives us the best of both worlds. To get there, it helps to understand how we evolved, what we are designed for, and how to get the most out of our body, mind, and spirit.

CHAPTER 2

Creation of the Caveman and the Early Environment

So, let's put things into perspective and look at who we really are from an evolutionary standpoint. This includes the environment in which we evolved, how we evolved to meet the demands of that environment, how our environment has changed, and how it is similar. We will examine the critical success factors for surviving in that environment and how those factors helped us survive to create the world we live in today. Having set this context, we can explore how to adapt these success factors to today's environment and thereby ensure our current success and the passing on of our genes to future generations.

First, let's look at our planet. The planet Earth is approximately 4.5 billion years old. The earliest hominins (human-like primates) appeared approximately 7 million years ago. Homo sapiens (modern-day humans) appeared approximately 100,000 years ago. To put that into perspective, if the planet Earth were an hour old, hominins would have appeared 6 seconds ago and modern human beings would have appeared less than 1 second ago.

In plain English, it literally took forever for our primate ancestors to appear and, from there, almost 7 million more years for them to evolve into us. Comparatively speaking, we are a fresh, young new species that has not changed anatomically and physiologically in the last 100,000 years. However, our environment and the way we live have, and they continue to change dramatically. The purpose of this chapter is to discuss the factors that have led to our current evolutionary status, our success in surviving, and the factors we need to focus on to ensure our continued survival and future evolution.

As you can see above, the existence of humans is rather brief in comparison to the existence of the planet Earth. To further bring things into perspective, dinosaurs came into existence, evolved, and became extinct over a period of 183 million years versus hominin's 7 million years and counting. Basically, dinosaurs existed 176 million years longer than we have thus far. If we think of setting world records of staying in existence, dinosaurs are in an extremely comfortable lead. In fact, I think a Las Vegas odds maker would strongly favor dinosaurs based on probability alone. The emphasis I wish to make here is that we are a young species and, as such, are relatively inexperienced in regard to harmonizing with our environments—natural or created. Because the environment in which we live continues to change, we too, must continue to change in order to successfully adapt, survive, and excel.

Change and Success

Throughout my research, one point has been emphasized over and over regarding the success of Homo sapiens' ability to outlive their cousins such as the Neanderthals and Homo erectus. The main reason why we Homo sapiens have succeeded is due to our *ability to adapt to change and ability to develop skills and tools to help us better adapt to change.* It should be noted that our ability to adapt to change remains our number one critical success factor today. In fact, this point will be emphasized throughout the book.

Let's first examine the environmental changes and how we adapted physiologically, anatomically, and psychologically since the inception of hominins. Over the past 7 million years, the hominin environment has been dominated by ice ages, which presented cold, harsh weather, with ice sheets in the northern hemisphere and extreme aridity in the tropical regions. Although there were interglacial breaks lasting about 10,000 years in between each ice age period, the weather was still harsh and not as we know it today. The severity of each ice age would strongly put a halt to all human development. Evidence shows that during one ice age, the human global population was as low as 10,000. If you can imagine, this would be the population a small town. Due to our ability to adapt, change, and survive such harshness, humans have been called an Ice Age species by some anthropologists.

Another key aspect of the environment in which we evolved was the fact that hominins were easy prey for the many carnivores that roamed the earth. These included saber-toothed tigers, huge serpents, and giant crocodiles. Imagine an environment that at any given time when leaving home for hunting and gathering, humans stood the chance of being dinner for one of these creatures. As a result, we developed a nervous system that could handle such high levels of stress. The switching of gears to deal with such stress is called *the flight-or-fight response* and is something we still possess today. Although the fight-or-flight response helps deal with danger and short-term survival, staying in this state too long will compromise your health. Even though most humans in the corporate jungle are not exposed to danger daily, there are other events that trigger this response—such as deadlines or managers that motivate by instilling fear into coworkers. Being able to control the fight-or-flight response is as key to good health and your ability to excel in today's corporate jungle as it was in the real jungle. Because our CNS (central nervous system) controls the fight-or-flight response and our body's ability to maintain optimal health, healing, and longevity, we will discuss how the CNS works, what we can do to help it, and what we should avoid doing that will inhibit its function in Chapter 4. However, before we do that, it may be helpful to discuss the corporate world and the logic behind it—and to understand how and why it can seem like a jungle.

CHAPTER 3

Knowing Your Corporate Jungle

As every good caveman knew, one underlying fundamental to survival was knowing and understanding the jungle. This included knowing the landscape, weather conditions, flora, fauna, fellow cavemen, predictable events, and unpredictable events. Knowledge was and still is power. It did not make sense to prepare for lion attacks or to train to pick coconuts if you lived in a temperate climate. Correspondingly, you need to know the corporation within which you work and understand the skill sets needed for survival in that particular environment. To gain that knowledge, it helps to review a few fundamentals upon which corporations are based. This includes how they operate, the resources available, the driving force behind their activities, and the criteria for making decisions. Depending on your experience, you may wish to skip or quickly scan the next two paragraphs as the information may be obvious and something you deal with daily. However, you may find it is worth reviewing if your department or function is isolated, causing you and your coworkers to lose perspective as to how you fit into the big picture. This can lead to poor coordination of corporate resources, duplication of efforts, and lack of cooperation. Reviewing this chapter will also give you a deeper perspective on Chapter 14, which suggests that you manage your own life by the same principles discussed below.

All corporations begin with human beings and an idea for a product or service. The idea is then tested to see if there is a market to make it profitable. This includes financial analysis and projections to forecast potential profits, associated costs, potential opportunities, and possible threats. Corporations may start out as small companies comprised of a few individuals and ultimately grow into global enterprises employing tens of thousands. At a small company, a few people may do all functions. However, as a corporation grows, these functions must be delegated and departments begin to grow in order to take advantage of economies of scale. As you can imagine, coordinating all of the functions required to support a single corporate mission becomes increasingly challenging as the company grows over time. This calls for careful planning and teamwork. Most corporations will break out each function into the following departments:

1. Strategic Planning

2. Marketing and Sales

3. Accounting and Finance

4. Information Technology

5. Operations

6. Human Resources

The strategic planning department typically consists of select members of upper management, the board of directors, the chief executive officer, chief of marketing and sales, chief financial officer, chief of information technology, chief of operations, and chief of human resources.

Just as a corporation starts with ideas, the strategic planning department will continuously discuss new ideas, which are validated in much the same way. Once validated, a strategic plan needs to be designed, coordinated, and executed. This means implementing the plan in the marketplace and generating sales revenue by the marketing and sales department. Further, such sales must be supported by operations; accounting and finance need to record and evaluate the sales; information technology needs to ensure requested information is available for decision-making; and human resources needs to ensure there are enough adequately trained people to support all transactions. Each new idea will present change, and change is challenging.

From my experience as a management consultant, it seems that no matter how well a change is presented and strongly justified and supported, there will always be resistance, an area overlooked, an unexpected lack of resources, and the list goes on. It is said that the only thing constant in a corporation is change. This is the nature of our modern corporate jungle. However, as discussed in Chapter 2, this is no different than an actual jungle or earthly conditions since the beginning of time. Accordingly, as that chapter notes, our *ability to adapt to change and our ability to develop skills and tools to help us better adapt to change* remains our number one critical success factor, even in the modern corporate jungle of today. So, not only do we need to be adept at performing our expected daily work, we also must be prepared to perform new and unexpected tasks.

As you can imagine, this type of environment is justly called the *corporate jungle* as it has many opportunities to trigger your CNS into a fight-or-flight response. In my experience, it can be so extreme that many people live in a constant state of fight-or-flight. This has detrimental effects on their ability to focus on work, as well as on their health. This is a lose-lose situation: people are at risk of losing their jobs due to poor performance and even poor health, and low productivity and high healthcare and disability costs can reduce a corporation's odds of survival. It is worth mentioning that workers under the age of 30 may be more resilient to being in fight-or-flight and most health issues tend to show up at age 30 and up. It is at this point that people wonder what happened to cause health problems, as they are not doing anything different. The point is that it takes time for health to deteriorate, and that the good lifestyle practices that we are going to discuss should be started as soon as possible to maximize optimal health, healing, longevity, and productivity while minimizing downtime, sick leave, and medical and disability costs. This is a win-win situation for the worker, the corporation, and our society. Let's now discuss the CNS and what can be done to produce a winning environment.

CHAPTER 4

Your Central Nervous System—Key to Success

A human being's CNS is like a computer's central processor: it basically controls all the functions of your body, from speech and movement to kidney and liver functions. Not only is the CNS instrumental in maintaining your health, but *maintaining your health is instrumental in maintaining a properly functioning CNS.* You cannot expect your CNS to maintain optimal health if you are not willing to take measures to stay healthy and make its job easy. This direct relationship is quite simple and is essential to our well-being. This relationship has become quite clear to me through my continuous research in correlating the fundamentals of Traditional Chinese Medicine with today's knowledge of human physiology. In fact, understanding and applying this concept is the underlying success factor in many of my patients' treatment plans. It is such a powerful concept in maintaining optimal health and success in life that I find the extent to which it is overlooked puzzling. Indeed, this fact itself compelled me to both write this book and speak on the subject to raise public awareness and help society beyond what I could achieve through my one-on-one treatments alone.

The major reason this concept is widely overlooked is that the CNS is mainly discussed in medical textbooks. Most people will never read a medical text book, and most medical professionals do not have time to explain how the CNS works. Accordingly, I have devised a practical explanation of the CNS's function that you can easily understand and apply. In fact, it is my patients' expressed gratitude and the successful clinical results achieved after applying these concepts that drove me to present them as part of this book. A full understanding of the CNS and how it affects health (and vice versa) is key to keeping us happy, healthy, productive, and successful in the corporate jungle and beyond.

The CNS: A Simplified View

The CNS has two states of operation. One is homeostasis, or what I call the state of *optimal health, healing, and longevity*. You experience this state during moments of peace and when everything seems to be going smoothly. This state of operation allows all your health maintenance functions to achieve optimal performance. The other state is that of fight-or-flight. In this state, things seem chaotic, such as during emergencies. During these times, your *health maintenance functions* are compromised, while your *survival functions* are at peak

16

performance. As you can imagine, if you are always in a state of emergency or having a fight-or-flight response, the CNS's ability to heal and maintain good health will be compromised. As I emphasize to my patients, the best way to heal any condition is to get your CNS to do it for you—after all, that is what the CNS is designed to do. The secret to optimal health, healing, and longevity is therefore, to stay out of the fight-or-flight state. To do this, we must first understand how the CNS works.

Directly or indirectly, the CNS controls all our health and bodily functions. The CNS begins with your brain and is supported by three systems:

1. The Somatic Nervous System

2. The Autonomic Nervous System

3. The Sympathetic Nervous System

The Somatic Nervous System

The somatic nervous system is the part of your CNS responsible for all bodily functions that you *have control* over. These are mainly movement and speech. You can imagine that the somatic nervous system is especially important to athletes, musicians, and other professionals who must make precise movements at precise moments. When an athlete or musician is stressed—and perhaps in a state of fight-or-flight—they will not perform as well simply because their CNS is preoccupied with other issues and cannot provide the usual resources to empower the somatic nervous system. Stress can affect the rest of us in the same manner and can determine whether or not we have a good day.

The Autonomic Nervous System

The autonomic nervous system is that part of the CNS responsible for all those functions that you *cannot directly control* or those functions that should happen *automatically*. A short list of these functions is liver function, kidney function, production of red blood cells, digestion, reproduction, heart rate, breath rate, level of endorphins, level of adrenaline, and the process of sweating. Just as stress and fight-or-flight can adversely affect our physical performance and speech, they can also negatively impact all the health functions controlled by the autonomic nervous system—that is, liver and kidney function, digestion, heart rate, and so on.

The Sympathetic Nervous System

Technically, the sympathetic nervous system is part of the autonomic nervous system; its function is to constantly scan our environment for danger or life-threatening events and trigger the entire nervous system into the fight-or-flight state. As I noted above, the fight-or-flight state can inhibit physical functions, mental functions, and all health maintenance functions to increase your survival functions (as discussed below). Therefore, it is important for us to learn how to shut off a fight-or-flight response and return to the state of optimal health, healing, and longevity when appropriate. Let's now take a closer look at how this works in Table 4.1.

As you can imagine, the list of essential health functions that can be inhibited by the sympathetic nervous system's fight-or-flight response is vast. Following is a discussion of how a fight-or-flight response may be triggered.

Table 4.1 Simplistic View of the Central Nervous System

Part of the CNS	Function	Examples
1. Somatic	Controls bodily functions we have control over	Movement, speech
2. Autonomic	Controls bodily functions we do not have direct control over and that should happen *automatically*	Liver, kidney, production of blood cells, digestion, reproduction, heart rate, breath rate, hormonal balancing, sweating
3. Sympathetic	Scans for messages indicating danger or life-threatening events and triggers a fight-or-flight response, which inhibits functions of the autonomic and somatic nervous systems to enhance survival functions	Increases heart rate, breath rate, endorphins, adrenaline, sweating

Triggering a Fight-or-Flight Response

The sympathetic nervous system is always scanning for danger; traditionally, the biggest life-threatening event that we have all evolved to handle was a saber-toothed tiger attack. Such an attack would immediately send the entire CNS into the fight-or-flight state and compromise all bodily functions *not* related to survival. To follow our earlier CPU analogy, this is similar to the way a computer puts unnecessary functions into sleep mode or hibernation when they are not needed. In terms of the autonomic nervous system, this decreases health maintenance functions, such as our kidneys filtering blood, since if the battle with the tiger is lost, there will be no blood to filter. Similarly, the liver slows down on detoxing, digestion shuts down (in fight-or-flight, we burn glucose reserves instead of calories from food), and reproduction shuts down (this is no time to be thinking of procreating). Conversely, functions related to survival double up: heart rate increases to circulate blood for better muscle and brain function; breath rate doubles for extra oxygen; endorphins increase to numb any pain from inflicted injuries; adrenaline increases to speed up reaction time and endurance; and, since the latter produces heat, sweating increases as well.

To recap, fight-or-flight increases survival functions and decreases essential health maintenance functions. So, if you become accustomed to living in the state of fight-or-flight, you will be living with impaired essential health maintenance functions. You can do this only for so long before a health issue arises. In our 20s, we are typically starting our careers and working in fight-or-fight mode can be addictive, offering extra adrenaline, mental focus, and so on. Our bodies are also more resilient to stress, and we might not immediately suffer any health issues. However, by the time we hit our 30s and 40s and on up, the effects of living and working in the fight-or-flight state will take its toll. These effects differ for everyone, depending upon both job environment and individual genetic makeup. Some may suffer from migraine headaches, while others are hit with digestive problems. Likewise, some people may develop carpal tunnel syndrome, while others suffer from back and neck pain. The list goes on—and, the longer we continue living in fight-or-flight, the more problems we will likely experience, leading to a lack of productivity and disability in the work force. This can be detrimental to both individuals and corporations alike. It can also be prevented by learning how to avoid fight-or-flight and live instead in the state of optimal health, healing, and longevity.

Today, we do not have saber-toothed tiger attacks; the typical trigger of a fight-or-flight response for corporate workers today revolves around emotional excesses usually related to their career, relationships, and family. In addition, traffic, bills, unexpected expenses, and commercials telling you that you *need* something (and thus will get more bills) can all contribute to triggering a fight-or-flight response. This is primarily due to the fact that people react 20 times stronger to emotional stimuli than to intellectual stimuli, because emotions trigger your imagination and can cloud reality. Many times, a small emotional issue—such as a minor disagreement with a spouse—will be stored in our memory and remain unprocessed due to its overall lack of urgency. However, if you have 20 minor issues dwelling unprocessed in your memory and all are linking with the imagination, you can create 20 mountains from these 20 molehills and, in essence, create the same intensity of one saber-toothed tiger attack. The fight-or-flight state this triggers will adversely affect your essential health maintenance functions and your ability to coordinate bodily movements, speech, and mental focus. *It is therefore essential to learn how to end a fight-or-flight response and return to the state of optimal health, healing, and longevity.*

Stopping a Fight-or-Flight Response

To stop a fight-or-flight response, I have devised the Three Steps to Optimal Health, Healing, and Longevity as follows:

1. Resolve Emotions

2. Practice Daily Quiet Time

3. Regulate Your Diet

Resolving emotions clears your memory of any unresolved emotions that may have triggered (and continue to feed) a fight-or-flight response. Practicing daily quiet time nourishes your body, mind, and spirit, while allowing time to cultivate positive thoughts and inspirations that help you avoid a fight-or-flight state. Finally, regulating your diet gives you sufficient calories from food consumed to support your daily activity levels and thereby avoids burning the internal glucose reserves typically burned only during a fight-or-flight response. A poor diet can force your body to burn glucose reserves, thereby triggering your CNS into thinking there is an emergency and triggering a fight-or-flight response. Learning how to end or avoid a fight-or-flight response is key to optimal health and excelling in the corporate jungle.

Summary

As a human, you inherited a CNS that evolved to deal with an environment that was overwhelmed with daily life-threatening events. Your CNS has two states of operations. The state of optimal health, healing, and longevity is for peaceful, pleasurable, and constructive moments; it gives you full coordination over movement, speech, mental focus, and your health maintenance functions operate optimally. The state of fight-or-flight is for life-threatening events; it gives you enhanced survival functions, but compromises your essential functions for optimal health, healing, and longevity. In addition to being triggered by danger, a fight-or-flight response can be triggered by excessive emotions or irregular eating patterns. To avoid existing in this highly tense state and decreasing your health accordingly, you can learn how to manage your emotions and eating habits using the Three Steps to Optimal Health, Healing, and Longevity—that is, resolving emotions, practicing daily quiet time, and regulating your diet.

Following these three steps allows you to stay healthy and excel in your personal and professional lives. In the next section, I will describe the three steps in detail and suggest practical ways for implementing them into your daily life.

Part 2

Three Steps to Optimal Health, Healing, and Longevity

Prelude

Prelude

As discussed in Part 1, evolution has resulted in humans being engineered with the potential to survive a life of ice ages and saber-toothed tigers. Our success has come from our ability to adapt to change, often with the help of a fight-or-flight response that helps us fend off danger. However, it is just as important that we can return to the state of optimal health, healing, and longevity for success. Although life-threatening events are rare in today's corporate world, excessive emotions and irregular eating can drive your body into fight-or-flight. The problem is that these two scenarios are subtler than an attacking tiger, and thus it might not be obvious when you enter the fight-or-flight response. Therefore, you may not know enough to end it. For many of us, the fight-or-flight response has become the status quo state, which has a deleterious effect on both our health and our ability to succeed.

In the following, I discuss the Three Steps to Optimal Health, Healing, and Longevity and how to practice them. I also discuss the key benefits of avoiding the fight-or-flight state:

1. You stay more focused and enjoy the present moment.

2. Your stress threshold increases, helping you stay calm amidst adversity.

3. You are better able to cultivate intuition, creativity, cognitive skills, the inner genius, and the ability to proactively avoid stressful events in the future.

Where Chapter 1 discusses a day in the corporate jungle while in a fight-or-flight response, this section closes with Chapter 8, which describes a day in the corporate world while practicing the Three Steps to Optimal Health, Healing, and Longevity.

CHAPTER 5

Step 1—Resolve Emotions

As I described earlier, excessive and unresolved emotions are the most common triggers of a fight-or-flight response and compromise our mental focus, health, and ability to succeed. Therefore, it makes sense that the first step to coming out of a fight-or-flight response is to learn to resolve your emotions. The best way to resolve an emotion is to do something about it—that is, to take action. To this end, I have developed a tool that simplifies the process. All you need is a pen, a piece of paper, and your imagination. My tool is called a *PAD*, which is an acronym for:

1. Problem

2. Action

3. Date

To make a PAD, begin by creating three columns on a sheet of paper. In column one, make a list of what could possibly be bothering you—that is, create a list of *problems*. In column two, make a list of what you could do about each problem—that is, create a list of corresponding *actions*. In column three, make a list of when you can complete all the actions—that is, create a list of corresponding *dates*. The process of writing everything out with a chronological solution in black and white lets you interpret what is going on intellectually, without excessive emotions. Your intellect can then override your imagination's propensity to cloud the issues and thereby give you a clearer picture of reality. Typically, this clear picture of reality helps you attain a sense of peace, as things are often not nearly as bad as you assumed. This sense of peace is furthered by the fact that you will have created a chronological solution to your problems, which increases your focus and clarifies your goals. Most of the time, creating a PAD is sufficient to end a fight-or-flight response, which may emerge subtly over time due to excessive emotions. Next, you simply need to prioritize the actions on your PAD and manage your time to complete them, which can bring a lasting sense of peace. (For a full discussion on time management, see Chapter 9)

Certain types of situations tend to trigger excessive emotions and thus fight-or-flight. Generally, these situations fall into three categories:

1. Careers

2. Relationships

3. Family

Other areas that can further contribute to emotional excesses include traffic, bills, unexpected expenses, and advertising—whether on the radio, TV, or the Internet—which often aims to create a sense of need in us that can ultimately lead to more stress. Healthcare issues can also create excessive emotions and trigger the fight-or-flight response. In any case, we are constantly bombarded with emotional stimuli. If not immediately resolved, the emotions these stimuli foster can stay in your subconscious and adversely stimulate your sympathetic nervous system. In the table following is a list of typical emotions that can be triggered by issues related to our careers, relationships, and families.

Category	Issue Causing the Emotion (Problem)	Emotion
Career	Need a raise to buy a bigger house for family	Frustration, suspense, inadequacy as a parent, anger, inadequacy as an employee, low self-esteem
Career	Never-ending emails during non-work hours	Annoyance with lack of privacy, anger with inability to focus on family, fatigue as your mind

Category	Issue Causing the Emotion (Problem)	Emotion
		cannot rest, frustration with decreased quality of life, sense of burden from work constantly beckoning
Career	Excess traffic and commute time	Frustration from wasting valuable time
Career	Allergies due to faulty ventilation at work	Frustration with discomfort and poor work performance while dealing with allergies; fear it could be or turn into something worse
Career	Injuries due to repetitive motion at workplace	Fear of becoming disabled if you lose use of arms and/or wrists.
Career	Obesity due to unhealthy food and no time to exercise	Fear of aging and heart attack, lack of self-esteem, feeling lethargic due to effects of extra weight,

Category	Issue Causing the Emotion (Problem)	Emotion
		frustration with effects on love life
Career	Bored with your job and no career path to look forward to	Frustration of wasting life away
Career	Job does not allow for self-expression	Frustration of becoming a robot
Relationships	Spouse has to work excessive hours, leaving you without quality time together	Fear of loss of love life, fear of growing old, fear of being alone, frustration with lack of intimacy, fear it will get worse and lead to divorce, fear of wasting life away
Relationships	You and your boss do not have common interests	Frustration and discomfort with not being able to connect on a personal level, fear that the boss will not like you, fear that you will not be treated as favorably as

Category	Issue Causing the Emotion (Problem)	Emotion
		someone who does connect with the boss through common interests
Relationships	No time to see your friends	Frustration of wasting life away, frustration with loneliness, sadness due to loneliness, depression due to loneliness, frustration with lack of community outside work
Relationships	No time to form new relationships	Depression due to loneliness and lack of intimacy
Family	Not enough quality time to spend with family	Fear of wasting life away working and no quality time with family, frustration of being an inadequate parent

Category	Issue Causing the Emotion (Problem)	Emotion
Family	Family members imply that you are not living up to their expectations	Lack of self-esteem, feeling of inadequacy, anger and jealousy of other family members
Family	Not enough money and resources for education	Feeling of inadequacy
Family	Not enough money and resources to satisfy them	Feeling of inadequacy
Family	Children or other family members have behavioral problems or health problems	Frustration of feeling helpless, fear of consequences, loss of faith
Family	You have a health or behavioral problem and cannot do what you used to do to support family members	Frustration of feeling helpless, fear of consequences, loss of faith

Does any of the above sound familiar? Is it any wonder how emotional excesses such as these can make you feel like a saber-toothed tiger is on the perimeter, waiting for lunch? Hopefully, these scenarios clarify how emotional excesses can drive you into a fight-or-flight response. As discussed in Chapter 4, it is also clear that staying in a state of fight-or-flight will erode your health and the ability to excel. Although the above examples taken together might seem hopeless, they are a reality for many people—and the reason why I refer to the corporate world as the *corporate jungle*. Moreover, the effects of each of these issues can be minimized once you examine the emotions triggered by them and do a PAD to resolve them.

Given these examples of problems that may trigger a fight-or-flight response, you are now prepared to make your own PAD with your own personalized list of problems. It is important to be imaginative here; many problems that bother us and thereby trigger a fight-or-flight response might be in our subconscious. Thus, you may be unaware of those issues and their respective prominence in your life. To address this, write down everything you can possibly think of. The more items you write, the more will come to mind. This will increase your ability to focus on those big items that, when resolved, may resolve other items. For example, you might have a negative attitude that you have been harboring from childhood, self-imposed limitations that others may have convinced you of, or lack of confidence that may need building. The list may seem endless, but it can bring about a sense of self awareness that you may have never thought possible.

As mentioned above, the best way to resolve an emotion or related problem is to do something about it, transforming those emotions into actions. After making your list of problems, you can make a list of corresponding actions that will resolve or minimize them. That said, it is wise to remember that sometimes there is nothing you can do about a problem but accept it. By accepting and embracing that problem, you can minimize the adverse emotional effects of continued resistance or denial that are driving you into a fight-or-flight response.

Finally, set realistic dates by which you can complete each action and lay each problem to rest. For some actions, the date may be specific, while for others it may be more general. For some actions, you can start immediately and the date can be *now*. For other actions, the date may be *next week, next month*, and so on. Remember to be realistic, make future estimates, and as future dates approach, get more specific. Overall, your objective is to do something about the problem—and thus the related emotions—rather than forget or procrastinate taking action, which will only perpetuate the problems and the stress they create.

The objective of a PAD is to add structure to a seemingly chaotic state by putting everything in black and white with a chronological solution. This allows your intellect to interpret your situation and minimizes the exaggerated and adverse effects of your imagination. A PAD allows you to gain a sense of peace and confidence by writing everything out and taking inventory of your emotions. This will end a fight-or-flight response and return you to the state of optimal health, healing, and longevity that will contribute to your ability to succeed. As an example, I used the above case scenario to create the following PAD and demonstrate how helpful the process can be.

A PAD engages your intellect, minimizes the adverse effects of the imagination, and brings a sense of peace.

Problem	Action	Date
Need a raise to buy a bigger house for family	Make yourself as happy as possible in your current living space	Now
	Stop comparing your situation to other people	Now
	Consider less costly options, such as an addition, bunk beds, or building out a bathroom	Over the next month
	Meditate, pray, or chant for a solution to come to mind (see Chapter 6)	Now
	Use other methods discussed in Chapter 6	Now
Never-ending emails	Set up boundaries that you will not answer emails immediately upon receipt during your personal time or daily quiet time;	Starting now

Problem	Action	Date
	decide instead to answer them in batches every hour, every two hours, or whatever fits your circumstances (on vacation, for example, once or twice a day is understandably acceptable)	
	Turn off your phone when necessary	Now
	Before you answer emails, sit down and center your thoughts. Decide not to get emotionally involved with the content or the answer, and decide that, after you respond, you will immediately forget the matter and return to your activity	Now

Problem	Action	Date
Excess traffic and commute time	Consider carpooling or mass transit alternatives	Now
	Change commuting times if possible	Now
	Find alternative routes	Now
	Listen to audio books or other forms of entertainment	ASAP
	Consider relocating	Over the next year
	Consider finding a new job closer to home	Over the next year
	Accept and embrace the traffic and commute	Now
Allergies due to inadequate ventilation at work	Make sure it is truly the ventilation at work by first seeking treatment for allergies and other cures	Within a month (as soon as an appointment is available)
	If treatments do not work and	After appointment

Problem	Action	Date
	ventilation is for sure the problem, discuss alternatives with human resources	
	If no solution can be found, consider finding a new job	Over the next year
Injuries due to repetitive motion at work place	Seek treatment	ASAP
	Discuss matter with human resources	ASAP
	Consider ergonomic solutions	ASAP
	Do therapeutic exercises to maintain health of related tissue	Now
	Eat right, exercise, and take supplements for optimal health of tissue (see options in Chapter 6)	Now
Obesity due to lack of healthy food and time to exercise	Embark on a weight loss program	Now

Problem	Action	Date
	Buy healthy foods	Within a week
	Make meals at home	Within a week
	Exercise	Now
	Review Chapter 6 for tips on these and other options	Now
Bored with your job and no career path to look forward to	Compare alternatives, then reevaluate current situation	Within one month
	Pursue other opportunities	Within one year
	Keep your job and satisfy your passions with hobbies and other interests, new or old (see Chapter 13)	Within one month
Job does not allow for self-expression	Compare alternatives, then reevaluate current situation	Within one month
	Pursue other opportunities	Within one year

Problem	Action	Date
	Keep your job and satisfy self-expression needs with hobbies and other interests new or old	Within one month
Spouse has to work excessive hours, eliminating your quality time together	Discuss and commit to set aside quality time for each other	Now
	Practice daily quiet time with each other (see Chapter 6)	Now
You and your boss have no common interests	Learn to accept and appreciate your boss for who he or she is	Now
	Increase rapport by learning about your boss's interests	Within one month to year
	Discuss your interests through other relationships	Now
No time to see your friends	Commit to spending quality time with friends periodically, even if it's just once or twice a year	As soon as arrangements can be made (perhaps within one month)

Problem	Action	Date
	Text or communicate with friends through social media	Now
No time to form new relationships	Commit to making new relationships	Now
	Use online methods, such as dating services or meet-up groups	Now
	Join organizations related to both personal and professional interests	Within one month
Not enough quality time to spend with family	Commit to setting aside quality time for your family	Now
	Practice daily quiet time with each other (see Chapter 6)	Now
Family expressed opinions that you are not living up to their expectations	Do not be affected by other people's opinions of you	Now
	Form and live up to your own expectations	Now

Problem	Action	Date
	Learn to be happy and have a positive attitude (see Chapter 15)	Now
Not enough money and resources for education	Encourage children to study more in order to obtain scholarships	Now
	Offer children a fun vacation if they get all A's and a scholarship (vacations are cheaper than education)	Now
	Redefine educational needs	Over the next year
Not enough money and resources to satisfy family	Talk with family about reality and ways to have fun within a budget	Over the next month
	Meditate, pray, and chant for more money (see Chapter 6)	Now
	Convince everyone to have a positive attitude (see Chapter 15)	Now
Children or other family members	Get attention ASAP; get involved	Now

Problem	Action	Date
have behavioral or health problems	in their healthcare and encourage them to overcome health issues	
	Investigate public schools that have more resources to correct behavioral issues at a young age	Over the next month
	Meditate, pray, and, chant for a solution (see Chapter 6)	Now
You have a health or behavioral problem and cannot do what you used to do to support your family	Redefine your objectives in life and make appropriate changes	Over the next month to year
	Communicate with family members so they understand what is going on	Over the next month
	Work as a team and a family unit to overcome voids	Over the next month
	Meditate, pray, or chant for a solution (see Chapter 6)	Now

Summary

Hopefully, you will not be experiencing all the above at once, but these problems and related emotions are a reality for many people. Making a PAD engages your intellect, minimizes the adverse effects of the imagination, and can bring a sense of peace and hope to otherwise seemingly desperate—or simply nagging—situations. Once you have completed a PAD, you can use it as a basis for a to-do list for time management purposes (see Chapter 9). This to-do list will help you to prioritize and take the appropriate actions. As you complete each action, you will gain more confidence and a stronger sense of peace. Keep in mind that you can make a new PAD anytime you feel emotionally overwhelmed, and then simply start and continue to execute on it. This should become part of your lifestyle. Soon you may notice that you are taking actions before problems start. You may also notice that you will be enjoying life more in the state of optimum health, healing, and longevity.

Writing a PAD is the first step to ending a fight-or-flight response and returning to the optimal health zone. As I describe in the next chapter, the second step is to practice daily quiet time. The more consistent you are in practicing daily quiet time, the less frequently you will find yourself needing to do a PAD.

CHAPTER 6

Step 2—Practice Daily Quiet Time

The second step to staying in the optimal health, healing, and longevity zone and avoiding or ending a fight-or-flight response is to practice daily quiet time. The emphasis here is on daily, as quiet time is not necessarily quiet. The more consistently you can practice daily quiet time, the less often you will find yourself needing to do a PAD. Quiet time is time to nourish your body, mind, and spirit. It is time to step out of the trees and to look at the forest. It is time to think about your life's purpose, what you have done to contribute to that purpose, and what you can further do to contribute to that purpose. Daily quiet time is an opportunity to clear any negativity you may be harboring by forgiving those who may have crossed your path in a negative way. It is also an opportunity to clear guilt by forgiving yourself for having crossed someone else's path in a negative way. You can then start to visualize how you would like to see your life in the future. This practice lets you replace negative harbored energy with hope and inspiration. From my experience, if you can practice daily quiet time for 60 consecutive days, your mind will then be more cognitively aware of the present moment, enjoy the present moment, and stay focused in the present moment. You will also be more intuitively aware of stressful events while they are brewing and be better prepared to proactively either avoid those events or avoid having a fight-or-flight response to them. Correspondingly, you will live more in a state of optimal health, healing, and longevity, which will allow for greater success and enjoyment of life.

Examples of Daily Quiet Time

Daily quiet time can be practiced in many ways. As mentioned above, the emphasis should be on nourishing your body, mind, and spirit. However, some practices are more intense than others and each can serve a different purpose. In the table following are some of the more common forms of daily quiet time and their corresponding benefits.

Activity	Benefit
Meditation	Nourishes mind and spirit
Prayer	Nourishes mind and spirit
Chanting	Nourishes mind and spirit
Qi Gong, Yoga, and Tai Qi	Nourishes body, mind, and spirit

Activity	Benefit
All exercise	Nourishes body and mind
Watching a peaceful movie, reading a good book, or listening to relaxing music	Nourishes mind and spirit
Singing or playing a musical instrument	Nourishes mind and spirit
Experiencing joy and laughter	Nourishes mind and spirit

The objective is to find what works for you. You may find that what works for you changes over time and therefore you might change your routine. That is fine. The most important thing is to practice quiet time *daily*. Below is a discussion on each of the above types of daily quiet time with some insights and resources.

Meditation

Meditation and prayer have been around for as long as human records go. The reason they have endured is because they are powerful and they work. Meditation can be practiced in many ways, and many of my patients ask for instructions; however, I really do not think any one form has proven to be better than another. The most important thing is to start with one form and do it consistently. Practicing 10 minutes of meditation daily is exponentially better than no meditation at all. One basic method of meditation that I practice is outlined as follows:

1. Set aside a time to do meditation daily. Be consistent. It all depends what time of day works best for you. For

some it's early morning. For others it's after lunch, after work, before or after dinner, or perhaps before bedtime. The only way to find out what works best for you is to try out various times.

2. Find a place that is quiet and peaceful. This could be your own little corner, room, or place in the outdoors.

3. Prepare yourself by stretching. You can do some or all the qi gong stretches discussed in Appendix A as preparation. You might like to take a shower first, wear lose clothes, light a candle, burn incense, play peaceful music, or do all the above.

4. Find a comfortable position. Traditional meditation methods suggest a position where your spine is erect to allow your chakras, or energy centers, to align in a harmonious way. You can do this by either sitting in the lotus position favored by yoga practitioners or by simply sitting erect in a chair with your back straight and not hunched forward.

5. Increase the oxygen in your blood stream with breathing exercises. You can do this by breathing in through your nose and filling up your lungs completely while counting to eight, holding your breath completely for eight seconds, and then slowly breathing out through your mouth for eight seconds until your lungs are completely empty. I also find it helpful to visualize during your breathing exercise. Following are a few examples: a) When breathing in, visualize that you are breathing in *relaxation*, and when breathing out, visualize that you are breathing out *stress*. b) Visualize breathing in healing golden light, and breathing out darkness. c) Get creative and visualize breathing in

something you want in your life (such as love, happiness, abundance, or success) and breathing out any feelings or issues that cause lack of these. I suggest at least eight of these types of breaths. However, you can do as many as you like.

6. Next, sit quietly and begin your meditation. This is a great opportunity to reflect on your life's purpose, what you have done to contribute to it, and what you could further do. This is also a great time to reflect on forgiving others and yourself for any wrong doing and visualizing how you would like to see your life in the future. In her book, *Ask and It is Given*, Esther Hicks suggests that, whatever you focus on, doing it for a minimum of 68 seconds offers maximum therapeutic effect. It is at this point that I like to have a timer to keep me centered and focused, as well as to let me know how long I am focusing on any given point. One useful tool for this is an app called the "Mindfulness Bell," which you can set to ring at defined intervals during your meditation. You can have fun and experiment with meditation, visualizing aspects you would like to see more of in your life (as in the breathing method I recommended above). Also, once I have meditated on a topic or emotion, I like to observe and watch for hints about how it may begin to manifest in my life. These hints might come in the form of helpful situations, people, events, and circumstances (SPECs) that appear or occur with synchronicity. I discuss this SPECs concept further in Chapter 15, which focuses on having a positive and winning attitude. Remember: your intention is most important here. If you have good intentions, something good will always come from your meditation. Just be patient and mindful to look for it.

7. To close your meditation, I recommend you visualize and express thanks for all that you have to be grateful for in your life. It's important to avoid taking things for granted; when you take the time to express thanks and be grateful, you open the door to even more opportunities and reasons to be grateful in life.

These seven steps are just one method of meditation that I have found to be fruitful in my life. However, many other methods exist; to find them, you can simply search the Internet or buy CDs, digital files, or digital apps with guided meditations. You can even record your own guided meditation. Find what works for you and have fun.

Prayer

I do not think prayer needs to be explained in any depth. Prayer is like meditation, in that it has stood the test of time; however, prayer is more structured and focused. Depending on your belief system, you may have grown up learning many prayers for many purposes. You may have your favorite prayers, or perhaps you can find one that you like by searching the Internet. You can also make up your own prayers in a traditional format to address your particular situation. Or you can write your own prayer in the form of a short poem, mantra, or affirmation. You can say your prayer silently or aloud consistently throughout the day. Then, as with meditation, look for SPECs that allow the object of your prayer to manifest in your life. With consistency and good intentions, the power of prayer to nourish body, mind, and spirit cannot be underestimated. The reason the concept of prayer has been around since our caveman days is because it works. Use prayer wisely.

Chanting

Some see chanting as a way of praying through singing. Chanting can be in the form of words or meaningful vibrations. Tradition holds that when we express our intentions or prayers with the vibrations of the voice, it helps better prepare the way for them to metaphysically manifest into our reality. Chanting can be just as fruitful as meditation and prayer. There are many forms of chanting, including chants from ancient Sanskrit, Native American tradition, Gregorian monks, and so on. You can do an Internet search and find one that works for you. You can change to something else anytime you feel it is appropriate. One of my favorite forms of chanting is to sing the old camp song "Kumbaya." If you are not familiar with this song, you can find it online to learn the melody. The song allows you to chant for any subject you wish to attract by putting it in the lyrics. For example, if you want more love in your life you can sing the words as follows:

> Someone is *loved* my lord, kumbaya,
>
> Someone is *loved* my lord, kumbaya,
>
> Someone is *loved* my lord, kumbaya, Oh lord, kumbaya.

Instead of love, you can fill in any word or concept you feel is appropriate. It takes about 25 seconds to sing a verse, so if you want to apply the 68-second concept as discussed above, I recommend singing at least 3 verses for whatever concept you are chanting for. (In case you were wondering, kumbaya is African slang for *come by here*.) Again, with consistent chanting, we can look for helpful SPECs as manifestations of our intentions into our physical reality. And, like prayers, you can make up chants and sing them whenever you want. Have fun— but be aware: if you chant in front of your coworkers, you may have to give them a copy of this book to show them that you still have your sanity.

Qi Gong, Yoga, and Tai Qi

When done right, qi gong, yoga, and tai qi all help nourish the body, mind, and spirit. Of the three, I find qi gong to be the most practical, as yoga requires a special mat and clothes and tai qi requires approximately 150 square feet of space. Qi gong can be done almost anywhere and in any clothes. In fact, I have done qi gong on airplanes during long flights or in my office as a break after extended periods of time either with patients or concentrating at my desk. Qi gong works by combining breathing exercises with movements and postures that stretch all major muscle groups. It thus improves the following:

- Flexibility of muscles

- Circulation to your brain, muscles, tendons, tissues, bones, nerves, and organs

- Peripheral nerve conduction

- Relaxation of your entire CNS

Although there are many different methods of qi gong, I devised a simplified version of what is commonly referred to as the Eight Treasures. My simplified version is made up of eight postures, as illustrated in Appendix A. While doing qi gong, I also enjoy doing the above chanting or breathing exercises. However, qi gong can be done listening to music or in pure silence. As you work with my simplified version, you may wish to advance by taking a class or just keep it simple and consistent. Like meditation, 10 minutes of qi gong is exponentially better than no qi gong at all. In any case, pick what works for you and stick with it. The important thing with any form of daily quiet time is that you actually do it daily.

Exercise

All exercise is a great form of daily quiet time. You might like walking, jogging, weight training, or playing a sport. All are good and have something different to offer. While walking may be more relaxing and calming to the mind, jogging is more physically demanding and releases *feel good hormones* (such as dopamine and endorphins) into your system. However, both are good for cardiovascular strength and to increase circulation. On the other hand, weightlifting is great for maintaining muscle strength and bone density. Additionally, weight training can be relaxing and rewarding, and can build confidence. Playing sports can do any or all of the above, depending upon the sport. However, team sports offer the added benefit of belonging to a community, which is very important for our health as humans. Obviously, with any exercise, you must not overdo it and must make sure you are in good enough physical condition to participate. Joining a gym may be a good place to start. Like all other forms of daily quiet time, make sure you enjoy it and that you do it daily.

Reading, Movies, and Music

Reading, movies, and music are all great forms of daily quiet time. Naturally, you should be discerning about what you read, watch, or listen to. A horror movie or scary book may not serve much good other than to make you realize how wonderful life is in reality. However, I do not recommend this approach. I think it is much more fruitful to watch a calming movie or read an enriching book. Thus, a movie that reinforces your ideals and goals would be a better form of quiet time. The same goes for music. From my experience, it is better to listen to uplifting music than music that expresses disturbing emotions. Of course, it all depends on what works for you. I am not saying never see a scary movie, read a scary book, or listen to controversial music. I am simply saying that my experience has shown them to not to be the best form of daily quiet time.

Singing or Playing a Musical Instrument

In the Taoist philosophy, singing is the voice of the heart, and it is often said that music is the voice of the soul. What better form of daily quiet time could you have than to speak from the heart and soul? In addition, scientific research has demonstrated with functional MRIs that almost every part of the brain can be stimulated at once when singing or playing a musical instrument. The logical left side of the brain tackles the mathematical precision involved with music, while the more creative right side is used when improvising with music or when expressing through melodies, keys, and notes. In addition, when singing or playing an instrument, the visual cortex is used to read music, look at keys or strings, and watch the audience; the auditory cortex is used to listen and express with sound; and the motor cortex is used in the precise physical movements of fingers, arms, lungs, and so on. Using all of these parts of the brain with music is creative and therapeutic. Therefore, singing or playing music is considered one of the best forms of daily quiet time. If you learned to sing or play a musical instrument as a child, you may wish to start again. However, it is never too late to learn something new. Have fun, be a rock star!!!

Experiencing Joy and Laughter

Joy and laughter are the best medicine. There is nothing like being with friends and laughing. It can be in any venue, with any activity, including dancing, playing a board game, playing cards, or telling jokes. Being with friends gives us a sense of community and a sense of belonging that are two very important aspects for optimal health, healing, and longevity.

Being carefree, joyous, and laughing helps us to forget our stresses and appreciate life. Do not forget to make time for friends, family, or other opportunities to let go, be happy, and laugh. It is a great form of daily quiet time.

Summary

These are just some of the many forms of daily quiet time. Be creative and find out what works for you. Also, you do not have to do the same form of quiet time every day. You can change things up to keep them interesting. Practicing daily quiet time will help express passion and develop a positive mental attitude. These are two key aspects of daily quiet time. In fact, expressing passion and having a positive attitude are so important that I have written a chapter on each in Part 3 (Chapters 13 and 15, respectively). Daily quiet time is time to nourish body, mind, and spirit. It is time to think of the big picture in life. It is a time to focus on your life's purpose on the one hand, and a time to let go and just accept life and be grateful for it as it is on the other. Although practicing daily quiet time should be done daily, it does not have to be quiet. Practicing daily quiet time can keep you out of the fight-or-flight response, increase your mental cognition, increase your threshold for stress, and allow you to be more creative, intuitive, and proactive in avoiding stress. Daily quiet time will help you stay in the mode of optimal health, healing, and longevity, while assuring your success in the corporate jungle.

CHAPTER 7

Step 3—Minimize Stress by Regulating Your Diet

The concept of regulating your diet to avoid the fight-or-flight state is a concept that is fundamental to human existence. However, from my experience, it is too often overlooked and under-applied in healthcare today. Learning how to regulate your diet is easy and the payback is great. For example, almost everyone has heard that breakfast is the most important meal and that a healthy diet consists of three square meals a day. Yet, how many of us challenge these principles? These concepts are fundamentals to avoiding a fight-or-flight response and staying in optimal health. They are also fundamental for weight management. However, while we have heard these concepts, most of us do not pay attention to them as the underlying principles are rarely explained.

In this chapter, I will explain why these concepts matter and teach you how to apply them in an easy-to-follow framework. Once you adopt a regulated diet, it takes only a few days to realize how valuable the benefits are to your health and ability to excel in the corporate jungle. In a few days, you will notice that you have increased focused, a higher threshold for stress, and more energy throughout the day and into the evening.

The best place to start is by becoming familiar with the following framework, which focuses on dieting for stress management:

1. The typical person burns approximately 100 calories per waking hour without exercise.

2. Carbohydrates are burned during the first and second hour after they are consumed.

3. High protein foods (those with 50% or more calories from protein) are burned during the third and fourth hour after they are consumed.

4. Fats are burned during the fifth and sixth hour after they are consumed.

5. The most you can burn is two hours (200 calories without exercise; see rule 1 above) of any food type (carbohydrates, protein, or fat) with each meal.

6. Avoid eating meals greater than 500–600 calories.

7. Eat breakfast within an hour of waking.

8. Avoid going to bed with unburned calories in your stomach.

9. Excess calories are stored as fat and slow down your metabolism.

10. Try to eat three 500–600 calorie meals a day, with snacks as necessary

Based on the above, if you are awake for 16 hours, you will require 1,600 calories from food to support your activity level without exercise. If you exercise, you may require more calories depending on your objective. If you are doing aerobic exercise to lose weight you may not want to eat extra calories. However, if you are doing anaerobic exercise such as weight training to develop muscle and strengthen bones you should eat extra calories—especially protein—to help build muscle tissue. Since the point of this chapter is to assist you in dieting for stress management without exercise, let's discuss a diet to support 16 waking hours, or 1,600 calories.

Rule 7 says to eat breakfast within an hour of waking, so if you wake up at 7:00 a.m., you should eat something before 8:00 a.m. My suggestion is to eat a 500-calorie breakfast as close to 7:00 a.m. as possible, making sure it contains 200 calories of carbohydrates, 200 calories of protein, and 100 calories of a fat. (For examples, see Table 7.1 under *Suggested Meals and Snacks*) According to the framework above, the calories will be time-released to provide energy to support activities as indicated in the following table.

Calories/Food Type (consumed at 7:00 a.m.)	Time Calories Will Be Released to Support Activity
200 Calories of carbohydrates	7:00–9:00 a.m.
200 Calories of a high protein food	9:00–11:00 a.m.
100 Calories of fat	11:00–12:00 p.m.

You will find that when you time your calories to burn as you need them in this way, you will be more mentally focused, more resilient to stress, and more energetic and productive—as well as better able to resist any junk food that may be offered throughout your office.

To keep the day going smoothly, you should have your lunch at noon, as this is when you will have burned all your calories from breakfast. I recommend that your lunch be structured the same as breakfast, except to make it a 600-calorie meal to release energy as indicated in the following table.

Calories/Food Type (consumed at 12:00 p.m.)	Time Calories Will Be Released to Support Activity
200 Calories of carbohydrates	12:00–2:00 p.m.
200 Calories of a high protein food	2:00–4:00 p.m.
200 Calories of fat	4:00–6:00 p.m.

This meal will give you a similar experience as the breakfast, with increased mental focus, resilience to stress, energy and productivity, and resistance to unhealthy snacks until 6:00 p.m., when you should eat dinner. Ideally, dinner would be another 500-calorie meal, structured for calories to release energy as indicated in the following table.

Calories/Food Type (consumed at 6:00 p.m.)	Time Calories Will Be Released to Support Activity
200 Calories of carbohydrates	6:00–8:00 p.m.
200 Calories of a high protein food	8:00–10:00 p.m.
100 Calories of fat	10:00–11:00 p.m.

The above structured diet will have allowed you to burn calories from food consumed in a time released sequence to support your activity level throughout the day. To give you a sense of what this food might consist of, I have chosen the following from Table 7.1 below (under *Suggested Meals and Snacks*).

Calories/Food Type	Time Calories Will Be Released to Support Activity
Breakfast (consumed at 7:00 a.m.)	
200 Calories of fruit	7:00–9:00 a.m.
200 Calories of protein powder	9:00–11:00 a.m.

Calories/Food Type	Time Calories Will Be Released to Support Activity
100 Calories of chia seeds blended with the above and water to make a smoothie.	11:00 a.m.–12:00 p.m.
Lunch (consumed at noon)	
200 Calories of bread for a sandwich (two slices)	12:00–2:00 p.m.
200 Calories of sliced turkey breast in the sandwich	2:00–4:00 p.m.
200 Calories of a fat from two slices of cheese for the sandwich	4:00–6:00 p.m.
Dinner (consumed at 6:00 p.m.)	
200 Calories of vegetables	6:00–8:00 p.m.
200 Calories of any meat, poultry, fish, or tofu	8:00–10:00 p.m.
100 Calories from olive oil used to sauté the vegetables	10:00–11:00 p.m.

The above diet is relatively simple, and it assumes you can eat your next meal when you need to. However, this is not always possible in the corporate jungle. Knowing how to work with the above framework can help you obtain the needed flexibility. The next section discusses how to be flexible with the framework and still make it work for you. Overall, a diet regulated using this framework has many benefits stemming from the benefit of helping you avoid a fight-or-flight response, which can be triggered simply by a lack of calories. As I now describe, not eating on time, under eating any of the food types, or skipping meals can trigger a flight-or-fight response that can hinder your productivity and health.

How Does a Poor Diet Trigger a Fight-or-Flight Response?

Eating to provide enough calories to support your activity level makes sense. However, you might be wondering where you get calories to burn if you do not eat on time or if you do not eat the proper amounts of carbohydrates, proteins, and fats to appropriately time-release calories. Without food, we have two primary internal sources of calories: body fat and glucose reserves. Although body fat is primarily burned during aerobic exercise, glucose reserves are primarily burned during a fight-or-flight response, which traditionally happened only during life-threatening events (such as a saber-toothed tiger attack). As Chapter 4 points out, during a fight-or-flight response, digestion shuts down, as it is too inefficient to provide the caloric surge we need to burn to defend ourselves during such an attack. Instead, our bodies will call on our glucose reserves.

Glucose is a form of sugar that is stored in our muscles and livers, where it is ready to be secreted into our bloodstream during an attack or other dangerous situation. We have all evolved to store about 1,500 calories of glucose—the approximate amount required to defend ourselves during a life-threatening event. To put this in perspective, it is roughly enough to run seven miles and is equivalent to a full day's worth of food.

In addition to a flight-or-fight response, our bodies will also draw upon glucose reserves if we do not eat enough.

Accordingly, from the time you wake up until the time you eat breakfast, you are burning your glucose reserves. If you do not eat breakfast within an hour of waking, you will burn 100 calories of your glucose reserve (see rule 1 above). This is enough to put your body in starvation mode and will trigger a fight-or-flight response. As Chapter 4 notes, once in a fight-or-flight response, we exit the mode of optimal health, healing, and longevity and may lose our mental focus, productivity, ability to deal with stress, and ability to maintain health. Thus, a poorly regulated diet can lead you to being in a fight-or-flight response regardless of how much you resolve your emotions with a PAD (Chapter 5) or practice daily quiet time (Chapter 6). Once you start burning glucose for energy due to a lack of food, it is tough to get back on track. Therefore, eating breakfast within 1 hour of waking is fundamental to a healthy diet.

Why Is Breakfast Your Most Important Meal?

How many times have you heard that breakfast is your most important meal without an explanation? Breakfast is the most important meal because once you burn your glucose reserves, you must replace them. It is a defense mechanism of our CNS. If you need calories and have not eaten, you will burn your glucose reserves. Once your glucose reserves have been consumed, the next time you eat, your CNS will signal all calories consumed to refill your reserves until the 1,500 calories have been replaced. After the reserve is replaced, your autonomic nervous system will signal your metabolism to burn the leftover calories to support your activity level. But what happens if you do not eat enough to replenish your 1,500 calories of reserve?

If you do not fully replenish your reserves, you will continue to burn glucose reserves and remain in a fight-or-flight response. By skipping breakfast, you run the risk of depleting your reserve to the point that you never fully replenish it at each meal. Thus, you may end up remaining in a fight-or-flight response all day long. This is the primary reason why breakfast is your most important meal.

The secondary reason is that, at the end of the day, if you are still low on glucose, you will have *cravings*—your body's way of reminding you to replace your glucose reserves. These cravings may cause you to overeat close to bedtime. If this happens, you will go to bed with undigested food in your stomach. In the long run, this can lead to many more problems.

When you sleep, all food should be digested and the nutrition of the food should be absorbed into your bloodstream. When you sleep, your body should be resting. Your body's primary activity should be the circulation of a nutrient rich blood stream to repair and nourish all your tendons, tissues, bones, nerves, and organs. If you have a stomach full of undigested food, this process is inhibited. In addition, digesting food during sleep will interrupt your sleep and may lead to poor breathing and snoring. Additionally, most calories digested in your sleep will be stored as fat. Finally, when you wake up, you may feel groggy—and the last thing your CNS will want to do is eat and digest more food. As a result, you might skip breakfast again and start the fight-or-flight process all over. In the long term, this will lead to a life of inadequate rest and inadequately nourished tendons, tissues, bones, nerves, and organs. This is an invitation for fatigue, sickness, obesity, and a multitude of health issues. This is why breakfast is your most important meal.

Why Three Square Meals Per Day?

In addition to hearing that breakfast is the most important meal, you have probably heard that you should have three square meals per day. Many of my patients inquire about eating multiple smaller meals every few hours. Although you can make either approach work, I prefer three square meals, as it has many advantages. Many of my patients are under the false impression that eating frequent smaller meals will speed up their metabolism. However, if these meals are all protein or all fat, they may not provide calories to burn for three or five hours, respectively, after you eat them. Hence, such meals would promote glucose burning and thus lead to a fight-or-flight response. As mentioned above, when in a fight-or-flight response, digestion and metabolism are shut down. If you were to eat every three hours, the only way to keep your metabolism going is to eat 300 calorie meals consisting of 200 calories of carbohydrates (to burn in hours one and two) and 100 calories of protein (to burn in hour three). This type of diet leaves no room for fats, which are essential to our health. Therefore, the small and frequent meal plan may be inadequate in the long term. Plus, in the corporate world, you may be too busy to eat every three hours and skipping meals will further lead to a fight-or-flight response. The best diet for your metabolism and health in the corporate environment is three square meals with 200 calories of carbs, 200 of protein, and 100–200 of fat each meal, with carbohydrate snacks as needed when you cannot eat on time. If you are on a special diet or under medical supervision for your diet, be sure to discuss this concept with your medical provider. You might find a trade-off that can give you the best of both worlds.

Why Should Your Snacks Be Carbohydrates?

The main reason your snacks should be carbohydrates is because, if you are eating three square meals as recommended, the snack's purpose is to stop glucose burning or prevent a related fight-or-flight response when you cannot eat your meals on time. For example, if calories from lunch are burned off by 5:00 p.m. and you will not eat dinner until 7:00 p.m., you should have a 100–200 calorie carbohydrate snack that will give you immediate calories to burn and thus avoid a fight-or-flight response. Not eating for two hours after your last meal is absorbed and the related calories are burned, launches you into starvation mode and triggers a fight-or-flight response. It should be noted that snacks such as nuts and cheese are both 80% fat and 20% protein. Since most of the calories are fat, they will not be digested and ready to stop glucose burning for five hours. Thus, they do not make good snacks. Healthy carbohydrate snacks include fruit, dried fruit, bread, crackers, vegetables, and some snack bars. Complex carbohydrates that are lower on the glycemic scale are the best, as they burn more efficiently. They're also less processed and higher in fiber, which ensures a more regulated release of the calories during hours 1 and 2 after they are consumed.

How Flexible Can You Be with the Framework?

There is room for flexibility within this framework; you do not have to follow it exactly. For example, not everyone burns 100 calories per hour. Therefore, through trial and error, you should figure out what works best for you. Working out—and your objectives for working out—will create variations, but they are relatively straightforward. The average person burns approximately 100 calories per waking hour. Thinner, more active people may burn a little more, while heavier, less active people will burn a little less. If you get hungry quickly and frequently with 100 calories, try increasing it to 125 calories (or even more). If you always feel stuffed and start gaining weight, you can decrease your requirements to 75 calories (or maybe less) per waking hour. If you want to gain weight, you can increase your hourly intake of calories; if you want to lose weight, you can decrease it. Losing weight in this fashion is much more comfortable and healthier for you than the many fad diets, which ignore the timing of calories burned based on food type. For example, many diets do not allow carbohydrates and may force you to burn your glucose reserves for energy. As mentioned above, this can trigger a fight-or-flight response that can in turn inhibit your health and leave you feeling uncomfortable while dieting. These types of diets cannot be sustained, and many people who try them end up regaining any weight they lost.

Another key factor to consider is how many hours you have been awake versus how many calories you have eaten. For example, if you ate breakfast at 7:00 a.m. after rising from bed at 6:00 a.m., then went to bed at 12:00 a.m., you would need 1,800 calories. If, as in the above example, you ate just 1,600 calories, you could afford to have a 200-calorie snack during the day or to eat an extra 100 calories each at breakfast and dinner. Given my experience, it is okay to be late or early by one hour for any one meal, to overeat an extra 100 calories at any one meal occasionally, or to have an extra 100 calorie snack occasionally without gaining weight or causing a flight-or-flight response. In other words, you will still be in the bell curve of acceptability. However, once you exceed these limits, you will go outside the bell curve and may gain weight or experience a fight-or-flight response and all its disadvantages.

The Digestive Function of the Pancreas

The pancreas is important in this process and can be viewed as an internal bio-chemist. The pancreas resides just below the stomach. Accordingly, once food is time-released after being broken down by stomach acid, it is presented to the pancreas for analysis. The pancreas will analyze the type of food presented (carbohydrate, protein, or fat) and release the appropriate digestive enzymes necessary to biochemically transform the food into a format that will facilitate absorption of the calories and nutrients by the intestines and then the bloodstream. It is important to note that upon absorption, this is the point of no return; if you cannot burn the calories absorbed, they will be converted to fat, and the only way to burn fat is with aerobic exercise. If you never do aerobic exercise, you will never burn the fat. Every 3,500 excess calories convert to one pound of fat. So, if you were to overeat 100 calories at every meal and not exercise, you would gain a pound of fat every 12 days (300 calories per day × 12 days = 3,600 calories, or about one pound of fat). This would equate to 35 pounds a year. Given the many sedentary jobs in the corporate jungle, it is easy to see how people gain weight in such an environment. Excess pounds from fat slow down your metabolism, make you lethargic, destroy your self-esteem, and make it easier to gain even more weight. These consequences further emphasize how important it is to eat just enough to support your activity levels and, if you want to lose weight, a little less. Also, as I noted earlier, humans can burn only two hours' worth of any food type, which translates to 200 calories (100 each hour) without exercise. However, you could increase this to 1,000 calories (500 per hour) if you were doing something intense, such as long-distance running, because your activity level changes your required calories.

Another important aspect of the pancreas is that, when you are in a fight-or-flight response, the pancreas—which functions in relation to digestion—shuts down. It thus will not release digestive enzymes. Without these digestive enzymes, food will not break down as effectively and may cause gassiness and bloating. Moreover, without digestive enzymes, nutrients contained within food may not be effectively absorbed. Thus, you could be eating the best food in the world and still be malnourished due to the impact of a fight-or-flight response on your pancreas.

Suggested Meals and Snacks

Learning what to eat for a properly regulated diet may seem daunting at first. For this reason, I have constructed the Table 7.1 below, which shows a variety of meals that are simple to prepare. Although preparing your own food is recommended, the meals in Table 7.1 are readily available in most restaurants or in the prepared food sections of supermarkets. Although this list offers variety, it may not be varied enough or accommodate specific needs. For this reason, I recommend learning to read food labels so that you can prepare and create your own meals and snacks. The next section will discuss the fundamentals of reading food labels.

Three square meals a day, keeps the doctor away!

Table 7.1 Suggested Meals and Snacks

Carbohydrates (50 g @ 4 cals/gram = 200 calories)	Protein Sources (50 g @ 4 cals/gram = 200 calories)	Fats (11 g @ 9 cals/gram = 100 calories)
Breakfast		
2-3 Slices of toast	4 oz. Smoked wild salmon	4 Tablespoons cream cheese
2-3 Slices of toast	200 Calorie protein powder shake (w/water)	Butter on toast
2-3 Slices of toast	2 Eggs plus 2 egg whites	Butter on toast
2-3 Slices of toast	2 Eggs plus Canadian bacon	Butter on toast
8 Crackers	8 oz. Nonfat cottage cheese	3 Tablespoons chia seeds
2 Bananas, 3 oranges, or 200 calories of any fruit	Blend fruit with 200 calories of protein powder and water	3 Tablespoons chia seeds
2 Bananas, 3 oranges, or 200 calories of any fruit	Blend fruit with 200 calories of nonfat Greek yogurt and water	3 Tablespoons chia seeds

Carbohydrates (50 g @ 4 cals/gram = 200 calories)	Protein Sources (50 g @ 4 cals/gram = 200 calories)	Fats (11 g @ 9 cals/gram = 100 calories)
Lunch/Dinner		
Sandwich (2 slices bread)	200 calories of meat, poultry, fish, or tofu	100 calories fat from cheese or mayonnaise
200 Calories of vegetables, rice, and/or grains	200 calories of meat, poultry, fish, or tofu	1 Tablespoon of olive oil or butter
Snacks (1 hour energy per 100 calories)		
Piece of fruit, dried fruit, juice with pulp, bread, crackers, vegetables, or grains		

Reading Labels and Creating Your Own Meals

Keep in mind that Table 7.1 is general and simplified. However, I do believe that the simpler you keep such things, the easier they are to follow. Although the table may not work for everyone, every time, it was constructed from information on food labels. To create your own meals, it is helpful to learn how to read and interpret food labels. The first information given on a food label is the serving size, serving size(s) per container, calories per serving, and calories from fat per serving. If you scan down the label, you will also find the number of grams of carbohydrates and protein per serving. Once you find this information, simply multiply the number of grams of carbohydrates and protein by four to calculate the number of calories per serving of each. For example, a label of frozen peas shows the following for each serving:

- 66 calories

- 0 calories of fat

- 12 grams of carbohydrates

- 4 grams of protein

To convert the grams of carbohydrates and protein to calories, simply multiply the grams of each by four. Thus, a serving of peas has 48 calories from carbohydrates and 16 calories of protein, for a total of 66 calories. As this example shows, a food is rarely 100% carbohydrate, protein, or fat. Therefore, I recommend categorizing each particular food based on the majority of the calories that it contains. So, in this case, most of the calories in peas are from carbohydrates, so you would count peas as a carbohydrate source. Thus, three servings would roughly satisfy the 200 calories of carbohydrates for a given meal. So, any food that contains 50% or more of its calories from carbohydrates, should be counted as a carbohydrate; any that contains 50% or more of its calories from protein, should be counted as a protein; and any that contains 50% or more of its calories from fat, should be counted as a fat. Remember, it is the rate at which stomach acid and digestive enzymes break food down and prepare it for absorption that determines when it will be burnable as energy. Thus, the major source of a food's calories should determine where it is categorized.

Now that you can create your own meals, you may wish to know some nutritional basics to further enhance your meals for optimal health, healing, and longevity. Following is a discussion of some basic nutritional facts for this purpose.

General Nutritional Information

The above diet recommendations are meant to be simple, offer essential nutrition, and keep you out of a fight-or-flight response—thus letting your CNS focus on optimal, health, healing, and longevity. Based on my experience with my new patients, maintaining a healthy diet may be the greatest step toward optimal health that the average person can take. Simply achieving this will put you light years ahead of a poorly planned diet. Having said that, I realize that you may be wondering about other aspects of nutrition and information on food labels that can further optimize your diet. In this respect, I have added the following for you to keep in mind:

1. Regarding carbohydrates, complex carbohydrates give a steadier burn than simple carbohydrates. If you are interested in taking your diet to the next level, go online and look up the glycemic index. Foods with a lower glycemic index are more complex, tend to have more fiber, and do a better job of keeping you out of a fight-or-flight response.

2. Regarding fats, avoid or minimize trans and saturated fats, both of which can cause high cholesterol. Instead, favor unsaturated fats, as they can lower cholesterol and are better for cardiovascular health.

3. Regarding meat and poultry, eat the leaner cuts and favor hormone- and antibiotic-free cuts whenever

practical to minimize the unwanted side effects of these substances.

4. Regarding fish, avoid farm-raised fish, as it contains more fat and less protein.

5. Eat organic and GMO-free foods whenever practical to avoid unknown chemicals and the side effects that non-organic and GMO foods may have on long-term health.

6. Regarding sodium, try to keep it under 1,500 mg per day to avoid high blood pressure.

7. Regarding fiber (both soluble and insoluble), try to take in about 25 grams per day as it is essential for digestion and healthy cellular formation throughout the body. You may wish to use a fiber supplement, as getting this amount can be difficult because many of our foods are over processed, causing a loss of fiber content.

8. Avoid or minimize foods that contain high-fructose corn syrup as much as possible; this type of sugar cannot be burned easily for energy and can contribute to excess fat storage.

9. Regarding vitamins and minerals, try to maximize them in the foods you eat. However, you may wish to take daily supplements just to ensure you are not deficient in any one area.

10. Take a probiotic supplement daily for healthy intestinal flora. A good quality probiotic requires refrigeration and guarantees at least 15 billion cells at time of consumption. When not refrigerated, the probiotic cells

begin to die off after they are packaged. To further support healthy intestinal flora, you should consider the following:

   a. a diet rich in probiotics, such as yogurt, kefir, kombucha, sauerkraut, pickles and pickled fruits, and vegetables

   b. drinking flavonoid-rich beverages, such as organic raw hot chocolate and green tea

   c. eating prebiotic foods that help make probiotics, including onions, garlic, leeks, dandelion greens, and raw asparagus

   d. drinking filtered water, as chlorine can disturb the balance of your microbiome and intestinal flora

11. Stay hydrated by eating fluid-rich foods and drinking water throughout the day. It is better to drink water one mouthful at a time to help absorb it. You can test for dehydration by pinching the skin on the back of your hand. If it is slow to return to normal you may be dehydrated.

Summary

Hopefully, you now understand why breakfast is the most important meal and why a healthy diet consists of three square meals a day. The goal of this chapter is to help you understand and implement the benefits of a regulated diet in helping you avoid going into a fight-or-flight response due simply to consuming insufficient calories or insufficient carbohydrates, protein, or fats in any given meal. You should have enough information now to start implementing a regulated diet right away. This chapter is not a complete guide to dieting and nutrition, and it is not intended to address specific medical conditions and diagnoses. My dietary recommendations simply aim to maximize your CNS's ability to maintain optimal health, healing, and longevity, while still providing yourself with excellent sources of nutrition. Keep in mind that you can eat the healthiest foods of the best quality, but if you eat them at the wrong times, you may end up in a fight-or-flight response and be unable to absorb the benefits of these foods. If food intake is not timed properly to match activity levels, the best nutrition intake in the world will still lead to fatigue and poor health.

CHAPTER 8

Life in the Optimal Health, Healing, and Longevity Zone

Because many of us live in a state of fight-or-flight much of the time, life in the optimal health, healing, and longevity zone can be a relatively unknown, unexplored place—a place some of us may have glimpsed while on vacation or perhaps during childhood, but that these days may seem like unfamiliar territory. When you live in the optimal health state, you enjoy all the benefits of an optimally functioning autonomic nervous system, including good circulation, good digestion, healthy skin and hair, and so on. You also enjoy the benefits of an optimally functioning somatic nervous system, including better physical coordination and more fluent speech. Simultaneously, your sympathetic nervous system has a higher threshold for stress so you will be less easily triggered into a fight-or-flight state. Because your CNS is not focusing on survival, your mind will be clear and relaxed, with a greater ability to stay focused and present in the moment. As you can imagine, this can be a game changer in life. Following are some examples of what life in the optimal health state may be like. You will note that the *Seven Skills for Excelling in the Corporate Jungle* as discussed in Part 3 are introduced here to demonstrate their value when integrated.

First, with an increased mental focus, you will be better able to focus on tasks at hand. This could be anything from an analytical spreadsheet at work to a moment of intimacy with your spouse. When you can focus with a clear mind, your imagination and creative genius are better able to participate in bringing a heightened sense of satisfaction and fulfillment to your work or other activities. This naturally causes positive feelings that, if harnessed and nurtured, will create a positive cascade that can breed confidence and ultimately success in all endeavors. Further, experience has shown that successful people with positive attitudes tend to breed more success—and more reasons to have a positive attitude (see Chapter 15). It is clear how this type of life would be much different than the picture portrayed in Chapter 1, "Drama of the Day in the Corporate Jungle," where confusion and negative energy seem to prevail. However, having an increased mental focus is only one aspect of the optimal health state.

Having increased coordination of movement, combined with the increased focus, could enhance your athletic ability. This could boost your golf game, tennis game, or any other physical activity. This benefit alone could add to your enjoyment of life and potentially fuel an upward cascade of positive energy. Increased coordination could also help if you play a musical instrument, which is an excellent form of daily quiet time. As discussed in Chapter 6, practicing daily quiet time will help maintain your ability to stay in the optimal health state. This means that you will be healthier and more successful in all aspects of life.

Let's take a minute to talk about the benefits of better control over your speech. Have you ever been lost for words or knew what you wanted to say, but just could not say it at a crucial moment—only to greatly regret it later? Being in the optimal health state will give you greater command over translating your thoughts into words. In addition to paying huge dividends in terms of better communication in the workplace (as discussed in Chapter 10), this will immensely benefit your relationship with your spouse and loved ones. To know what to say and when not only reflects on how intelligent you are, but it also helps you better persuade people and coworkers to support your projects and your goals, and thus leads to further success.

Above all, when we free our minds by cultivating and maintaining life in the optimal health, healing, and longevity zone, we allow ourselves to stay focused in the present moment. In this state, life is *real*—real in the sense that you are focused on the present moment, rather than allowing emotions and imagination to carry you away and use your resources to either worry about a past that you cannot change or stir anxiety about future events that may never happen. Further, by being better able to focus on the reality of the present and not on uncontained emotions that eat up imagination bandwidth, you will free up tremendous resources that can be focused on your intuition, which is a combination of the intellect and the imagination. As I discuss in Chapter 12, intuition is a powerful tool and an expression of our inner genius; it should not be overlooked. It is intuition that helps us see opportunities that are not obvious to everyone. Intuition also allows us to identify stressful issues while they are on the horizon, rather than after they invade our everyday space. This faculty lets us be proactive in avoiding stress, and thereby helps us preserve the optimal health state and our success. Life in the optimal health, healing, and longevity zone is an entirely different way of life than most of us know. This is sad as, in reality, this state is where life is meant to be lived. However, living in the state of optimal health, healing, and longevity is something that must be cultivated. At first, it will seem like an effort and you may feel like giving up. However, through persistence, this state becomes second nature, effortless, and you will want to live in no other way. Let's imagine what it might be like to live in a state of optimal health, healing, and longevity.

In the optimal health state, you wake up well-rested because you have no excessive emotions to pull your dreams into the nightmare zone. Instead, dreams are pleasant, and sometimes your intuition participates in a dream, allowing your subconscious to send messages to guide you in life. So, the first thing you do in the optimal health state upon waking is to write down your dreams in a journal and scan it for patterns you may have in your life or other messages about changes that might be needed or situations to pursue or avoid. From my experience, the more I write down what I dream, the more I remember my dreams and the easier it is to interpret their messages.

After journaling dreams, you might go to the kitchen and begin making tea, coffee, or organic hot chocolate. While waiting for the water to boil, you may do your qi gong exercises to wake up the body, mind, and spirit by stretching all muscles in preparation for the day and (when done daily) to ensure physical flexibility for life. This will also ensure that you

86

maintain good posture and thus preserve orthopedic health, as well as facilitate increased circulation to all parts of the body—including the brain, which will in turn help increase nerve function. Qi gong prepares your CNS to start its job of maintaining optimal health, as it receives and sends all signals via blood chemistry and nerve conduction. You might do your qi gong alone or with family members to deepen your relationships.

After qi gong you may wish to sit and meditate while you sip your hot drink. During meditation, you may wish to utilize the law of attraction to visualize and facilitate in creating a positive day. You may also wish to express gratitude for all you have. Just 10 minutes like this can help plant seeds for a positive attitude and positive day.

After mediation, you may wish to take 10 minutes to prepare and eat a breakfast: a protein shake with fresh fruit and chia seeds that offers 200 calories of carbs to burn in hours 1 and 2, 200 calories of protein to burn and in hours 3 and 4, and 100–200 calories of an unsaturated healthy fat to burn in hours 5 and 6 after consumption.

You then jump in the shower, confident that your breakfast is going to last and that you will not get hungry during meetings—or end up eating sugar and processed carb snacks, which seem to be prevalent in the corporate jungle to rescue people in a fight-or-flight state. You know you will not be one of those people, and it feels good. While in the shower, you chant to further cultivate positive vibes for a positive and successful day.

After showering, you dress and get ready for work. You want to look good to further your positive self-esteem and because you know that how you dress is a means of communication (see

Chapter 10). Therefore, your corporate culture may influence how you express yourself with clothes.

Your commute in the optimal health, healing, and longevity zone is a joy because you have been proactive and made sure it is manageable. You did this by moving to a community that offers mass transportation to and from your office, which allows you to listen to music, self-help podcasts, and chants—and even watch pleasurable videos. Or, you might work while commuting instead, and thereby be able to leave earlier to spend more quality time with your family. Some days, you work from home, which also allows less commuting time, more quality family time, and the ability to practice better quality daily quiet time during work breaks.

Whether working at home or in the office, you are more productive because you are well-rested, started the day with self-nourishing quiet time, and your stomach is full, freeing you to focus fully on all tasks at hand. Further, you practice value-added time management, considering your critical success factors that let you address all items on a timely basis without allowing anything to grow critically into the urgent and important category, as discussed in Chapter 9.

You love your workspace because you have designed and engineered it to support your business processes and implemented basic feng shui principals for added comfort, as discussed in Chapter 11. Not only is your workspace calming, it is uplifting and allows an even more enhanced opportunity for focus and efficiency. In addition, you have designed your desk, files, and computer files for optimal workflow given critical success factors and value-added management principals. You feel organized and prepared to do your job. Although you realize every day will not be a breeze, you are prepared mentally and physically in case of a surge in your workload.

You break for lunch about 5–6 hours after breakfast to avoid a glucose dip into a fight-or-flight state. You know how to eat, whether you bring your own food, eat out, or eat in the cafeteria. Lunch is another 500–600 calorie meal broken out into 200 carbs, 200 protein, and 100–200 calories of a healthy fat. You decide to eat 100 calories of green beans, 100 calories of spinach, 200 calories of chicken breast, and some olive oil on the veggies. That is plenty, and it will keep you productive and focused for the next 5 to 6 hours.

You have a productive afternoon and leave work feeling both challenged and stimulated. Your commute is as enjoyable and productive on the way home as it was on the way in. You arrive ready to commune with your family. Your spouse is in the optimal health zone as well and feels just as good as you do. It has even rubbed off on the kids and everyone knows the importance of a healthy dinner with some quiet time after. For dinner, you make sure not to overeat to the point where you will have undigested food in your stomach when going to bed. So, because you are eating at 6 and going to bed at 11, you will take in only 500 calories—200 of carbs, 200 of protein, and 100 of fat.

After dinner, you participate in your favorite form of quiet time. This may or may not include your spouse and children every night, but should include them a few nights out of the week. When you do include them, you make sure to choose forms of quiet time that they also enjoy.

When it is time to sleep, you go to bed feeling grateful for all you have and for all you have achieved. When you lie down, you are ready to sleep. Because all your food is digested, your body is ready to shut down and rest. At this point, your blood stream is richly loaded with all the nutrients it has absorbed throughout the day and, although your body will physically shut down, your blood stream will be busy circulating these nutrients to all your muscles, tendons, tissues, bones, nerves, and organs, making any repairs necessary and getting them all ready for the next day. With an empty stomach, your body will not produce excess heat and mucus, which may back up and constrict your bronchioles and sinuses. You will breathe clearly without snoring all night long. Because you have resolved all your emotions, your mind will be quiet during sleep and you will not have anxiety dreams. You know you will wake up in the morning fully rested and refreshed, ready to seize the day as the cycle of maintaining the state of optimal health, healing, and longevity continues.

Does life in the optimal health, healing, and longevity zone sound good to you? Naturally, every day will not be so smooth. However, if you persist at following the Three Steps to Optimal Health, Healing, and Longevity you will see more and more smooth days until they become the rule rather than the exception. Persistence is key and, as things fall into place, you will gain more and more confidence to continue and have a happier, healthier, and more successful career and personal life. In Part 3, we will discuss some additional skills that will further assist you in staying in the optimal health state, prevent the fight-or-flight state, and increase your productivity and success—all while assuring you excel in the corporate jungle.

Part 3

Seven Skills for Excelling in the Corporate Jungle

Prelude

In Part 1, we discussed how the corporate world can be so hectic that it could easily be compared to a jungle. We also talked about how we 21st century humans are still operating with a body and nervous system that evolved to survive in a real jungle, and how both have not changed for the last 100,000 years. We discussed how our CNS has two modes of operation: optimal health, healing, and longevity (for when times are good) and fight-or-flight (for surviving life-threatening events). We also discussed how, when in a fight-or-flight response, our ability to maintain health is compromised and that, in addition to life-threatening events, excessive emotions and irregular eating patterns can trigger a fight-or-flight response and compromise our health without us being aware of it. We further discussed the importance of practicing the three steps to optimal health: resolving emotions, practicing daily quiet time, and regulating your diet. In Part 2, we discussed, in detail, how to practice these three steps in our daily lives. However, in addition to these three steps, there are particular skills you can develop to further ensure good health, survival, and the ability to excel in the corporate jungle.

One fact brought to light in Part 1 was that we humans out-survived our Neanderthal and Homo erectus cousins through ice ages and jungle life due to *our ability to adapt to change and develop tools and skills to assist us in adapting to change.* In as much as skills such as tracking, hunting, gathering, fishing, fire-starting, archery, and spear-, arrow-, and tool-making were skills that ensured our survival in the real jungle, we need other skills and tools to survive in the corporate jungle. Some of the most prominent skills for the corporate jungle include time management, communication, workspace logistics, mental cognition, harnessing passion, personal resource management, and maintaining a positive and winning attitude. Part 3 will discuss these skills, what they mean, and how you can best take advantage of them to ensure your survival, health, and success in the corporate jungle.

In reading Part 3, you may decide that some skills are more relevant to you personally than others. Although each chapter is meant to be a sufficiently comprehensive discussion of each skill to help you implement it into your life, you may decide to read more or take a class in particular skill areas. Also, you may find a skill that is relevant to your situation that is not discussed here and decide to do further research. The objective is to remember the importance of being able *to adapt to change and develop skills and tools that help you adapt to change* and maintain optimal health and the ability to excel in your current environment.

CHAPTER 9

Skill 1—Time Management

After learning to live in the state of optimal health, healing, and longevity, it is now time to look at vital skills required to survive in today's corporate jungle. Time management is the first such skill. Time is a resource that you cannot replace. Once it passes, it is gone forever. Therefore, you cannot afford to waste time. Time management includes identifying all tasks that must be done and prioritizing them; this includes matching them up with your critical success factors and assigning a level of urgency and importance to each task. You will also want to forecast and allocate the necessary time to complete these tasks before you begin the execution stage. While executing your tasks, it is important to keep a log of how you spend your time.

Further, executing and completing tasks may be challenged by the fact that, before you complete the tasks you have identified, you will be given new tasks. This will require reprioritizing, etc. This is an ongoing cycle that will require timely communication with your coworkers, as discussed in Chapter 10. Through such communication, you can obtain additional information that will help you reprioritize your tasks. If you feel it will be impossible to complete all tasks in the allocated time available, your time management documents will help you substantiate a request for additional resources or negotiate a mutual compromise. Time management may seem like a lot of work, but you will soon discover how truly valuable and worth doing it is, if you wish to survive and excel in the corporate jungle. In practicing time management, you will not only learn to maximize your efficiency, you will also have substantive support for saying "no" if your boss tries to give you too much work. Being more efficient with your time and having a clear perspective on the time you have available will demonstrate your reliability and will help you develop stronger work relationships. With practice, you will refine your time management techniques, improve your productivity, and reduce stress while excelling at your job. Once you reach this level, you will find it difficult to waste time.

Identify Critical Success Factors

After making an entire list of tasks to be done, it is necessary to prioritize them before execution. The best way of prioritizing work tasks is to grade them based on the principles of *value-added management*. In the value-added approach, you identify the top five critical success factors of your company, department, or position (depending on which is most relevant). You then list each success factor in order of importance and assign each task to the most relevant critical success factor. For example, in my medical practice, the top five critical success factors in order, are as follows:

I.   Making Appointments for New and Established Patients

II. Patient Care

III. Maintaining Medical Supply Inventory

IV. Billing and Collections

V.   Administrative Tasks

The logic is as follows:

I.   *Making Appointments for New and Established Patients.* Because patients get better in the course of treatment, without new patients and new appointments for established patients as needed, my staff and I will have nothing to do. Therefore, anything related to making appointments for new and established patients is the highest critical success factor.

II. *Patient Care.* Patients who come to our office need proper care—otherwise, they will not get better, will not return, and will not recommend new patients. Therefore, after booking appointments, patient care is the next critical success factor.

III. *Maintaining Medical Supply Inventory.* To properly administer care for patients, we must have the appropriate medical instruments and supplies readily available for use. Without medical instruments and supplies, care cannot be properly administered, patients will not get better, they will neither return nor refer new patients, and we will have nothing else to do.

IV. *Billing and Collection.* To pay expenses and earn a living, my staff and I must get compensated for our efforts. Therefore, we must bill for services rendered and collect payments.

V. *Administrative Tasks.* We must pay our payroll, rent, supply vendors, etc., on a timely basis.

All of these tasks are critical to the success of my practice; however, as the list demonstrates, some have higher priorities than others.

Recently, I did a workshop for a company that makes components for the aerospace industry. That company's critical success factors are as follows:

I.   Quality

II. Timeliness

III. Price

IV. Flexibility

V. After-Sales Service

The logic is as follows:

I. *Quality.* If the company cannot provide quality components, there will be no demand for its products. In addition, given the industry, there is zero tolerance for poor quality components, as a defective bolt could lead to loss of lives and billions of dollars in aircraft and spacecraft investments.

II. *Timeliness.* If it cannot provide quality components on a timely basis, the results can be financially catastrophic, holding up production and increasing the production costs of its customers.

III. *Price.* Price must be competitive.

IV. *Flexibility.* It helps to be flexible, perhaps speeding up delivery, changing specifications, or doing other things within reason to accommodate unforeseen variables.

V. *After-Sales Service.* If all is done right, the company will not need to do much after-sales service, but it is still a necessary service for success.

As part of your time management program, it will help to identify your company's critical success factors. You should also identify the critical success factors of your department and your specific job. You might assume they all would be the same, however, your department and position may contribute to only one aspect of the corporation's critical success factors (such as billing) and therefore, you would need to develop only a subset of critical success factors. For example, at the above aerospace company, if you are in the billing department, your critical success factors may be as follows:

I.   Accurate Preparation

II. Timeliness

III. Collection

IV. Accounting

V.   Reporting

The logic is as follows:

I.   *Accurate Preparation.* Without accuracy, bills are useless.

II. *Timeliness.* If bills are untimely, it can lead to cash-flow problems and financial crisis.

III. *Collection.* If bills are not collected, it can also lead to cash-flow problems and financial crisis.

IV. *Accounting.* Without accurate accounting, none of the above efforts can be recorded and tracked; this can also lead to cash flow problems and financial crisis.

V.   *Reporting.* Without summarizing and reporting accounting records, they will be uninterpretable for key decision making and financial management, which can ultimately lead to cash-flow problems and financial crisis.

Once you identify your critical success factors, it may be a good idea to review your list with your boss since this is the person who will ultimately evaluate your performance and determine your chances of survival in the corporate jungle.

A second means of further prioritizing tasks, which was made popular by Dwight D. Eisenhower and by Stephen Covey in his book *First Things First*, is to classify them according to the importance/urgency quadrant below—that is, to classify them as either urgent, important, both urgent and important, or neither important nor urgent.

Tasks can be further prioritized by their level of both urgency and importance.

	Important	Not Important
Urgent	A. Important and Urgent	B. Not Important but Urgent
Not Urgent	C. Important but Not Urgent	D. Not Important and Not Urgent

Classifying tasks with a level of urgency and importance adds a new dimension to your priorities. For example, in my office, if I have two new patients who would like an appointment, and one has a medical diagnosis of mild insomnia, while the other can barely walk due to back pain, the back-pain patient would be given priority as the case is more urgent, even though both are important. Additionally, we might have two emails to answer to book two other new patients. However, if booking them means we will miss the cutoff to order timely supplies that are needed to treat them, then, while ordering supplies is a less critical success factor, it will be given priority as it is more urgent in this case. After all, it would not make sense to book the new patients if we do not have the necessary supplies. Further, ordering new supplies takes only 10 minutes, so doing this first will not eliminate our opportunity to book the new patients. So, again, while the appointments are higher in terms of their critical success factor, they can wait as they are less urgent.

Whenever possible, try to avoid allowing tasks to fall into Quadrant A: Important and Urgent, as these types of tasks are usually associated with high stress levels and completing them is usually compared to *putting out fires*. Working in Quadrant A may cause a fight-or-flight response and ultimately lead to burnout and health problems. Instead, you should manage your time to complete tasks while they are still in Quadrant C: Important but Not Urgent. When your focus is on completing tasks in Quadrant C, you will decrease the likelihood of tasks falling into Quadrant A. This will eliminate a lot of stress at work and prevent burnout and health problems. Life in Quadrant C should be your goal for a healthier, more successful life in the corporate jungle.

In addition to preventing tasks from falling into Quadrant A, you should avoid wasting time on activities in Quadrant D: Not Important and Not Urgent. Activities of this type include participating in idle gossip and the rumor mill, compulsively checking news updates, or scanning the Internet. Although you do not want to be considered a boring person, and it may be impractical to totally avoid idle gossip, keep your priorities in mind and do not waste too much time. You will be so much happier and successful in the long run.

Finally, it is worth discussing the types of activities that might fall into Quadrant B: Not Important but Urgent. These activities may not be important to complete a work task, but nonetheless might need to be addressed urgently. A perfect example of this would be if you have a toothache and must see the dentist immediately, or if you must work late and thus need to call your spouse to let them know that you will not be home as usual. Activities in this quadrant tend to be very important on the personal level, but not necessarily on the work level.

Also, remember to be flexible and sometimes bend the rules to be successful. An example of this would be doing a colleague a favor by assisting them to complete one of his or her Quadrant A: Important and Urgent tasks while delaying one of your own Quadrant C: Important but Not Urgent tasks. Although this deviates from your planned priorities, the gesture may be in the company's best interest overall and can help you build relationships. Following the above principles—and knowing when to be flexible—will build your productivity, make work a more enjoyable environment, and help keep you out of the fight-or-flight state.

Logging Your Time to Maximize Productivity

After prioritizing your to-do list and beginning to execute the completion of tasks, it is essential to use a time log to record how you spend your time throughout the day. This includes recording everything, including time to answer messages, chit-chat, take breaks, and (of course) to complete the tasks at hand. You can also quantify your level of productivity for each task on a scale of 1–10, with 10 being the most productive. Your objective in logging time in this manner is to identify when you achieve your peak performance levels and which activities inhibit your performance. You can use this information to proactively create and engineer productive scenarios and prevent unproductive ones. See the example of a log below.

Logging how you spend your time and the related level of productivity helps you identify both factors that promote peak performance levels and those that inhibit performance.

Time	Task	Critical Success Factor	Priority Quadrant	Productivity Level (Scale of 1-10)
8:00–8:15 a.m.	Read emails and listened to voicemails	1	A: Important and Urgent	10
8:15–8:30	Got a cup of coffee and gossiped with coworkers	None	D: Not Important and Not Urgent	0
8:30–845	Wrote prioritized to-do list	1	C: Important but Not Urgent	10
8:45–9:00	Returned high-priority voicemails	1	A: Important and Urgent	10
9:00–9:15	Gossiped	None	D: Not Important and Not Urgent	0

Time	Task	Critical Success Factor	Priority Quadrant	Productivity Level (Scale of 1-10)
9:15– 9:45	Returned high-priority emails	1	A: Important and Urgent	10
9:45– 10:00	Returned low-priority emails	3	B: Not Important but Urgent	6

From the above table, you could conclude that, by 10:00 a.m., you have been mostly productive but wasted 25% (one half hour) of your time. Therefore, you could reengineer your future mornings, making a point to stay focused and productive. Perhaps a mental break with gossip is good, but you may be more productive by waiting until you have accomplished more.

Keep the log going all day and make note of when you are most productive and which surrounding circumstances promote your highest productivity. You may notice that you reach your highest level of productivity when you are not disturbed for two consecutive hours. Therefore, it might help to reprioritize your time so that you are not interrupted by the phone, emails, texts, and gossip. For example, when I am at work seeing patients, I make it a point to turn off my cell phone and email notifications. At that point, my emphasis is on patient care; any interruption will disrupt a key critical success factor to my practice. Additionally, I ask my assistant to book patients as close together as possible, while leaving breaks every few hours. This lets me get into the treatment groove, and then later switch hats and get into a record-keeping groove. Having the time to get into a groove in each area makes me more efficient in both areas. I found this to be much more efficient than frequently switching hats throughout the day. The rewarding feeling of being on top your game will give you motivation to persevere and refine your time management skills.

Logging your time allows you to best structure and manage it in a way that most effectively meets your specific critical success factors. Further, making a prioritized to-do list for the next day at the end of your work day helps you start work in a more focused manner. This, in turn, helps you better control your schedule and complete all tasks in a timelier manner. The result is increased job satisfaction, which will spill into your personal life in a positive way.

Investing the Extra Time Created

So, what happens if you become so efficient that you create a significant amount of free time? My suggestion is to invest it in making your life easier by being proactive and allocating any newly created free time to tasks in Quadrant C: Important but Not Urgent. After analyzing your time log over time, you will discover which items in Quadrant A: Important and Urgent cause the most stress and how they come about, and thereby be able to proactively create a plan of action that will help you complete these tasks *before* they become urgent.

Another way of investing extra free time is to assume additional responsibilities to help your boss. As long as no one sees it as a threat, this will be helpful—and, when it comes time for promotions, you will have demonstrated your ability to perform the job. My only word of caution here is to use diplomacy in doing the next-level work. For example, if your boss comes into the office and finds you have just performed his or her tasks for the day in your spare time, he or she may feel seriously threatened. If so, you could either decide to slow your pace and enjoy more of the social aspects of work or find another job where good work habits are more respected and rewarded. There is no right or wrong decision in such cases; your choice may depend on many other variables. For example, you might need to make more money and thus need a higher position. In contrast, you might enjoy your current position for reasons beyond money. Or maybe you are simply not that aggressive, and just want the current paycheck. In any case, time management teaches you how to better manage your time, better perform your job, and ultimately put yourself in a position where you make educated decisions on how to best manage your career, rather than passively sit back and let someone else do it for you.

Managing Personal Time

Another aspect of time management that can also determine your chances of survival in the corporate jungle is your ability to manage your time outside of work. If you spend time outside of work in an enjoyable and rewarding fashion, you will show up to work more refreshed and ready to go than people who show up for work having wasted their time off. Therefore, it would be wise for you to identify critical success factors for your personal life and prioritize completion of them in much the same way as you would for work tasks. This applies both to recreation time and to personal responsibilities (see Chapter 14) for a further discussion on managing your personal life.

Summary

Time is one resource that cannot be replaced. Therefore, managing time is one of the most valuable activities you can do in life. Time management may at first seem tedious and cumbersome, however like everything else, it eventually becomes second nature and something you will do automatically, without consciously thinking about it. You may start by identifying your position's critical success factors, then categorizing your tasks by their associated level of urgency vs. importance. Using these two factors as a guideline, you can prioritize your tasks and complete them accordingly. Additionally, you will want to log your time to identify which factors make you most productive, and which cause you to waste time. Once you are on top of your game, you may create extra time, which you should strategically invest rather than waste. Time management should be applied to your personal life as much as your professional life. With refined time management skills, you will minimize going into a fight-or-flight response, maximize the state of optimal health, healing, and longevity, and ultimately create a longer, healthier, and more successful life in today's corporate jungle.

CHAPTER 10

Skill 2—Interpersonal Communication and Teamwork

Interpersonal communication and teamwork are another vitally important skill needed to survive in the corporate jungle. As mentioned in Chapter 3, one benefit of corporations—and an underlying reason for why they evolved—is that they harness economies of scale by having us *work as a team to achieve a common goal*. The fundamentals of teamwork include a clearly defined goal, a plan of execution, an effective leader or coach, solid communication, and timely and effective sharing of information to execute transactions in a smooth, coordinated, and timely manner. With solid teamwork, a strong sense of bonding and trust will develop. Moreover, solid communication among team members is essential to overall success.

Communication can be viewed as the act of sharing information, expressing ideas and concepts, and relaying emotions. It is important to note that you do not have to write or speak anything to communicate. In addition to knowing what, how, and when to communicate, it is just as important to know what, how, and when *not* to communicate to reach your goals. Effective communication requires being aware of incoming messages sent to you and acting upon them accordingly. This can be challenging as incoming messages are not always in the form of spoken words or a clearly written memo. Communication can make or break your career; listening to and understanding incoming messages and sending out appropriate responses is vital to your success in the corporate jungle.

It is important for you to remember that without the support of your teammates or coworkers, you can achieve only a fraction of your total potential. Moreover, without the support of your teammates or coworkers, you risk isolation, which can lead to the demise of your career in an environment where teamwork is an underlying fundamental. Too often, corporate managers are poor coaches or leaders, leaving goals poorly defined and dispersing individual efforts, causing conflict that may result in an uncoordinated free-for-all in a department or division. In any case, surviving and excelling requires good communication skills to know what your boss wants and what your objectives are, and then working with others to achieve both.

Good communication and teamwork require understanding goals and objectives, identifying and properly utilizing communication resources, knowing the members of your team (including their strengths and weaknesses), and knowing how and when to communicate effectively to successfully achieve goals. Simultaneously, it is important to understand how to communicate to motivate others and achieve common goals. Finally, you also should be prepared to effectively communicate in a way that discourages people who may be adversely affecting the achievement of common goals. As highlighted below, each aspect plays a key role in success.

Defining Goals and Objectives

The first thing you must do in any position is to identify your goals and objectives. In other words, identify what is expected of you and the skills necessary to do your job well and to ensure that it is perceived that way. This may be easy or challenging, depending on your boss and coworkers. Some bosses may have everything in writing and things may go well. However, what is in writing may have changed in reality. This can cause confusion, and it may represent differences of opinions that were never resolved. Regardless, such situations must be resolved through effective communication. In a very diplomatic way, you must verify the objective without causing conflict or resentment. If tension and disagreement exist among team members, this should be noted. You may not be able to do anything to resolve existing disagreements. If this is the case, the most you can do is make note of it and understand that it is a variable that you must consider when performing your job.

Let's say, for example, that the operations manual states that two signatures of approval are necessary to have a check written to pay an invoice. However, one of the people needed is usually traveling and not available for timely processing. Your coworkers may tell you not to worry about it and to ignore the manual as it was written by the auditors, and they do not understand how things get done. You may then have a discussion with your boss who claims that no matter what, two signatures of approval must be obtained. At this point—or when you can see a timing conflict with a payment arising—you should inform your boss that the other signer is rarely available and work out a resolution to meet your objectives and satisfy all concerned. If you were to continue by simply listening to coworkers, you would run the risk of being accused of not performing your job properly in the future.

As another example, let's say you are a salesperson and are told that all sales transactions must have a 30% profit margin. However, your largest customer feels they deserve a greater discount in light of volume. Instead of simply refusing and risk losing profits, you may wish to communicate with your boss and resolve the conflict with approval. Again, if you assume the risk by completing the transaction outside the defined scope, you expose yourself to being accused of not doing your job properly.

In the corporate jungle, it is often better to minimize this type of risk by securing approval. Also, it is important to remember that the definition of your goals and objectives may change as time goes on. Further, the established policies and procedures may need to be adjusted for certain transactions. You need to constantly be aware of these changes and resolve discrepancies through effective communication. If possible and practical, you should document communication in writing. This will ensure you achieve your goals and objectives without risking being told that you are not doing your job correctly.

Knowing Resources Available for Communication

When starting a new position, you need to recognize all the available resources for communication. These include email, texting, voicemail, group and one-on-one phone conversations, group and one-on-one meetings, casual gossip, and the so-called *rumor mill*. You must decide which level of communication is the most appropriate for what you need to convey or share.

An email or text is the least personable, as it lacks voice intonation from you and offers no opportunity for body language. Further, you cannot read reactions of the recipient and spontaneously address them. Emails and texts also can be forwarded endlessly. An email or text may be perfect for distributing directions to a client or announcing a meeting's time and venue. However, it may turn into a disaster as a means of gossip or to criticize someone or something. Voicemails are similar. Because recipients can hear your tone of voice, they are a little more personable. However, they too can be misinterpreted and distributed endlessly before a reaction or further explanation can be given.

Group meetings are convenient for distributing information to a controlled group with an opportunity to respond to several individual reactions. This makes them a superb venue for reaching a group consensus. However, anyone who disagrees with the group consensus will have made it known to the entire group. Hence, you should always be aware of the sensitivity of the topic discussed and have an idea of the general consensus prior to expressing your viewpoints. Depending on the topic, if you strongly disagree on a sensitive topic, it may be best to not express your opinion openly to an entire group if it is obvious that doing so will provide no value or will not change any policies. Instead, you may wish to bring it up after the meeting in a one-on-one confidential conversation with your boss, or discuss it with someone you can confide in to gain advice on whether it is worth further expressing your viewpoint.

A one-on-one meeting is the most personable venue, letting you clearly express both voice intonations and body language. Naturally, this type of meeting is for the most confidential types of topics, including job performance and evaluation, announcements of confidential upper management decisions, and personal conversations.

Gossip sessions are also very important, as they let you learn a lot about your teammates, including what motivates them, why they have their position, what their personal goals are, whether their personal goals conflict with yours, and so on. Gossip sessions can be used to build trust, but they can also destroy it.

Ultimately, regardless of the venue or the topic discussed, if you take your career seriously and wish to both survive and excel in the corporate jungle, you must always maintain a clear picture of the goals and objectives upon which you will be evaluated. Each topic brought up in any communication venue must be evaluated in terms of how it may help, hinder, or otherwise affect your ability to meet the goals and objectives of a job. You must also consider how expressing your opinion may cause others to perceive you. If expressing your opinion puts you in the minority and may cause others to perceive you as negative, it may be best to just go with the flow to ensure you will survive and excel. This is especially true on topics that will not affect your ability to perform your job and meet goals and objectives. The bottom line is that in the corporate jungle, to meet your goals and objectives, it is most often to your advantage to go with the flow, be politically correct, and avoid standing out in a negative way. Knowing your communication resources and how to use them can effectively manage this process.

Knowing the Members of Your Team

In starting any position, in addition to gaining a clear understanding of your goals and objectives and effectively using communication resources, it is extremely important to get to know the members of your team. We are all individuals and, in as much as we have similarities, we also have our differences. Neither fact can be ignored when your aim is to achieve success. The sooner you understand your teammates or coworkers, the better your chances of surviving and excelling in the corporate jungle. One of the best ways to learn about your coworkers is through casual conversation, eating lunch together, or participating in work-sponsored social events.

It is important to remember that, while it is human nature to want to help each other, work can be a competitive place. Therefore, do not always expect everyone to be there for you in every circumstance. In addition, many of us are dysfunctional at times and not able to constructively deal with the emotional ups and downs of work and life. Therefore, do not expect everyone to behave in the norm under all circumstances. At times, you may find yourself to be somewhat dysfunctional in some situations. Knowing this and doing something about it will keep you from shooting yourself in the foot and prevent you from being your own worst enemy as you try to survive and excel in the corporate jungle. Learning to harness the strengths of your coworkers and yourself—and to minimize the effects of everyone's weaknesses—will prove tantamount to a smooth and continuously blossoming career.

Knowing When, What, and How to Communicate

A useful concept, popularized in 1955 by psychologists Joseph Luft and Harrington Ingham, is to determine when, what, and how to communicate using the following *communication quadrant*, which categorizes everything we communicate into four quadrants as a combination of the following:

1. Things you know about yourself

2. Things you do not know about yourself

3. Things others know about you

4. Things others do not know about you

The Communication Quadrant helps to define when, what, and how to communicate.

	Things You Know About Yourself	Things You Do Not Know About Yourself
Things Others Know About You	I.	III.
Things Others Do Not Know About You	II.	IV.

It helps to categorize everything communicated from the perspective of this quadrant. Then, before communicating, stop and think about how discussing a topic may move it from one quadrant to another and the associated risk/benefit of such a move. For example, during any type of communication, you may share information that you know about yourself that others do not know. This may help you or work against you. At other times, you may be sharing something subconsciously that you did not know about yourself, but that is easily perceived by others. Through communication, others can share with you things that they have noticed about you that you were not aware of. Or, during communication, both you and others may discover something about yourself that neither of you realized before. As we communicate, information is constantly being transferred from one quadrant to another. It helps to always be aware of what is happening and weigh the risks and benefits involved in transferring information from one quadrant to another. Following are some examples.

Let's say your boss just told you that you are the best performer among your coworkers. Your boss shared this with you confidentially, and may not want the others to know as it might discourage them. However, you are quite excited with the news and, because you feel that you and your coworkers are good friends, you decide you want to share it with them. In doing so, you are moving information from quadrant II (things you know about yourself that others do not know) to quadrant I (things you and others know about you). The risk of sharing is that you will make it clear to everyone else that they are not the top performer, which might create resentment toward you. As a result, you might notice your coworkers not being as helpful as they once were. Thus, the risk associated by sharing this information is that it will make it more difficult to be the top performer in the future. Thinking in terms of the communication quadrant helps you foresee any associated risk in sharing information. In this case, by sharing the information, you make it more difficult to maintain your level of performance and destroy the happiness you gained when receiving the information. Clearly, the risk and negativity in sharing this information outweighs any of the benefit.

Sharing salary information can also fall into this category and should be avoided. The list goes on; you must always be aware of the risks associated with information communicated. At

117

times, coworkers may put you on the spot by asking you about your salary or other potentially sensitive information. The best way I can suggest avoiding giving out the information is to smile and politely ask them why they want to know. If they persist, you may simply state that sharing such information in your experience has never lead to a positive outcome and therefore you do not wish to discuss the matter. Anyone who cannot respect this is not interested in your own good. This should be a warning sign. As much as it may hurt to think that a coworker is more of a threat than a friend, it would hurt worse if this person were to use sensitive information you shared to hinder your career.

In the first example above, if your coworker were to tell you that he or she is the best performer, you would likely feel insecure in knowing that the best performer was not you. Naturally, any such information will be damaging, and you must determine how to react. It is best overall not to act in a negative way by working against your "better performing" colleague, but perhaps try to discover why they are perceived to perform better and attempt to emulate it. In doing so, you can better realize your full potential and either learn to be happy and accept the situation, or perhaps realize you may not be on the correct career path or have the best conditions to bring out your best performance. By paying attention to communication, both formal and informal, you can pick up such information, which can be used to make wise career choices. Making choices with wisdom will ensure that you survive and excel in the corporate jungle.

When communicating at all levels in a corporation, you must not only pay attention to the spoken word, but also to the tone of voice and, when necessary, try to determine the true intention of what is said. In addition to the spoken word, visual clues— offered through mannerisms, facial expressions, and things as simple as our clothes and hairstyle—can say a lot. These must not be overlooked; you must pay attention to the messages you are sending out and the messages you are receiving. This is important, as it helps you get to know your coworkers better, as well as ensuring that you send the right message to be perceived as positively as possible. It is all part of surviving and excelling. You need every edge you can get. Looking at people's mannerisms and clothing can help you determine how seriously they take their position. This, in turn, can determine their level of motivation and how likely they are to be an asset or liability to your own goals and objectives. For example, when people wear inappropriate clothing to work and are always laughing and joking, it could indicate that they are not very focused on or motivated by their job. Perceiving this, you might not want to choose such a person to cover for you when on vacation.

You also need to be aware of the image you are projecting through your own clothing and mannerisms. You need to be aware of both what the norm is for dress in your office, and what type of clothing will best project the right image for your position. The last thing you want to do is to project a not so positive or even a negative impression that you are not so into your job. This will cause others to perceive you much the same way you perceived the person above. This, in turn, could result in your being passed over for a raise or promotion. Keep in mind: I am not trying to promote phoniness here; however, just as a caveman hunting wild boar did not joke around or wear inappropriate clothing—such as ostentatious ceremonial costumes—during the hunt, you should look and act accordingly at work. If you find that it makes you uncomfortable to conform in this way, then you must ask yourself if you are in the right position. Your choice is to wear whatever and act however you want—and be willing to accept the consequences—or find a position where your personal taste in clothing and behavior is more acceptable. Although being in a place where you feel comfortable will strongly define your potential to succeed, you sometimes have to make practical compromises.

How you act and what you wear at work can greatly influence how you are perceived. If this is in anyway negative, it will make surviving and excelling in the corporate jungle more difficult. Survival is difficult enough under any circumstances. Therefore, you should be prepared to adjust to avoid negative perceptions and ensure that you survive and excel. Knowing what, when, and how to communicate is an essential skill to develop to thrive in the corporate jungle. Naturally, you would like to benefit from communication. However, communicating certain information may present risks that outweigh the benefits. Making use of the communication quadrant is an effective means of managing this process.

Using Positive Communication to Motivate Others

In addition to the above concepts, you need to be aware that what, when, and how you do and say things can motivate others to help you reach your defined goals and objectives. While carefully planned and strategic communication can help you succeed, spontaneous and unplanned communication can have adverse effects, leading to conflicts and lack of cooperation from others. Therefore, you should be aware of the fundamentals of how to best communicate to build cooperation and help you meet your objectives and goals.

One of the first things to remember when communicating is to always portray a pleasing personality. This can be done by smiling and being as friendly as possible. Another means of being pleasant is to call people by name. It has been said that no sound is more pleasing to people than hearing their own name. I had a firsthand experience with this when checking in at an airport, where the homeland security guard read my driver's license, looked me in the face with a smile, and stated "John B. Barrett." Immediately my eyes opened widely and a big smile spontaneously spread from cheek to cheek as I realized in a profound way how true this concept is. Therefore, try to be pleasant by smiling and using people's names. At the end of a conversation or phone call, if someone has been helpful, say thank you, followed by his or her name. If you do not remember it or did not get it at the beginning, ask them—and then thank them by name.

Another fundamental of communication when trying to motivate people is to always point out how they will benefit from doing the task at hand. Let's say, for example, that a key spreadsheet analysis needs to be done for a meeting the next day and you must ask a staff member to work overtime to complete it. Instead of directly asking them to complete the task as a huge favor, you could ask instead if they would like to be a key contributor to the team, as well as make the rest of the week go easily. Most people will automatically say yes to such a request; once they do, the rest is easy.

A most helpful principal in communication is to always understand your audience members and where they are coming from. If you do not know that up front, show interest and ask them about themselves. A good way to start a conversation is with one of the following six words: *Who, What, Where, When, How,* and *Why*. After showing interest by listening, you can then give feedback. This is a sure way to build a friendly bond. Even when giving a talk to a group of people, it is helpful to ask a general question of the group that people can answer by a show of hands. This makes people feel more a part of the talk and builds their interest and attention.

Remember, communication may not always be smooth sailing and at times conflict may exist. One thing to remember is to avoid arguing. If you are wrong, openly admit it and focus on discussing the solution as quickly as possible. If you must point out someone else's error, do not do it in an abrupt and abrasive manner. Try to put yourself in other people's shoes and understand that they did not do it on purpose and, like everyone, would like an opportunity to learn from their mistakes. Be subtle. Start by explaining the good things they have done and their positive attributes, and slowly work your way to the focal point of the error. Try to have them come up with a solution that they feel is their own. This helps to cultivate a positive attitude and makes them have more pride in their job. In the end, this will make them more dedicated and help them think things through a little more before making an error again. Simply put, whether praising someone or helping them to improve, by making people feel better about themselves, you cannot go wrong.

Another key aspect of communication when trying to build support and cooperation is to be enthusiastic with a sense of vision. If you are not enthusiastic about the task at hand, it may be difficult to convince others to get excited about it. Show some passion and excitement, and others will be more likely to jump on board with the same level of enthusiasm. If you can share a vision with enthusiasm, it will give your audience something more tangible to look forward to and make it easier to gain their approval.

Overall, when communicating to build cooperation and support from others, it is important to be pleasant, be personable, make them feel like an important member of a team, be compassionate and understanding, be constructive and help them grow, be positive, and show enthusiasm. Treat others as you would like to be treated for the best results.

Communicating to Discourage Adverse Personalities

You have to be naïve to think that, in a team environment with a competitive edge, no one would be thinking about how they can do better than you to get that next promotion. Therefore, you must always have your guard up and be prepared to calmly and precisely deter anyone presenting adversity. This is a skill that you need to be aware of and to develop. As mentioned above, many people in the workplace are dysfunctional and are willing to do anything to get ahead. If this means making you look bad, or simply be unwilling to help you, that might suit them just fine. You must be able to deal with such people quickly and efficiently. By understanding these people, you can learn to undermine their negative approach, put them in their place in a diplomatic manner, and discourage them from any future adverse actions. The techniques used in the previous section to motivate others will certainly help in minimizing anyone who may wish to undermine your efforts. However, there is usually at least one person who needs a little extra work.

These people come in different forms. Some people present themselves as angry, pushy, overly aggressive, and confrontational. Others may be rude, sarcastic, and try to make you look bad. Then there is the know-it-all who will try to trivialize everything you do and say. These types of people are like bullies. And, as you may know, the best way to deal with a bully is to put them in their place swiftly and efficiently. When in a corporate environment, diplomacy is of the utmost importance. The first and most important aspect of dealing with a bully type is to identify them as soon as possible. If you are naïve and try to ignore them, they will persist; the longer you ignore them, the more difficult a swift, efficient, and diplomatic response will become. In addition, bullies will take advantage of every opportunity to do more and more damage to your reputation. If you wait too long, it could be too late. Once you identify a bully (hopefully on the first strike), you should have a pocket response ready to let the bully know that you are not easy prey and that attacking you could make him or her look bad. An easy method I learned from a colleague long ago is the *listen, agree, pause, and conquer* approach.

Let's say a colleague, Bob, is rude, sarcastic, and tries to make you look bad in a meeting with an adverse comment. The first step is to *listen* and demonstrate that you heard Bob by repeating what he said; doing this can also serve to emphasize how negative he sounds. At this point, you *agree* with Bob, admitting that you can understand how he might feel the way he does. The next step is to *pause*. Finally, you *conquer* by stating that one would feel that way only if they were uninformed or did not quite grasp the full picture. You could then point out some obvious facts that Bob may have purposely overlooked in making his statements. This makes Bob look as bad as he really is. You can practice the listen, agree, pause, and conquer technique in everyday conversations as opportunities arise. Remember, you do not have to make anyone look bad; the real goal is to achieve your objective. When you get good at it, you can even turn some of the most difficult people into your biggest supporters. However, at the very least, using this approach lets bullies know that you are not an easy victim and neutralizes them as soon as you identify them.

In addition to the bullies, there are the lazy people that try to resist everything—from change to productivity. There are also the procrastinators, who never commit to or achieve much. Then there are the *yes* people, who commit but never deliver. Other common challenging types include the perpetual complainers, who are all smoke and mirrors, and the invisible people, who do nothing, say nothing, and are good for nothing. Again, like the bullies, you need to quickly identify these people and avoid having them on your team or having them play a part in your projects. If you cannot avoid them, do your best to give them less important, low-profile projects. From my experience, these people are difficult to change. If you can neutralize them and make them minimally productive, rather than their typical destructive selves, you will be a winner. To neutralize them, apply the principles discussed above. Be pleasant, personable, compassionate, and make them feel like important members of the team. Encourage them, and be constructive, be positive, and show enthusiasm. You may be surprised at how many you may win over. With all difficult people—bullies, lazy people, or otherwise—the most important thing is to identify them right away and apply the above techniques as soon as possible.

Summary

Communication and teamwork are extremely powerful and essential to surviving in the corporate jungle. The first step is to define your goals and objectives, and make sure all communications support them. Next, be aware of the resources and media available to communicate, understand the pros and cons of each, and use them to your advantage. It is vital to know the personalities of and generally understand your coworkers and team members, as this is key to knowing what to say, when to say it, and how to say it. You must always be positive in your communication and make others feel important. Simultaneously, you must be aware of any adversaries in the workplace and discourage them from dispersing your efforts as soon as possible. Effective communication and teamwork take practice. The first step is to be cognitively aware of the above guidelines and consciously implement them each day. Once rewarded by the positive results of good communication and teamwork, with continuous practice, these guidelines will become automatic and rewarding in the future. Clearly, good communication skills are essential to success in the corporate jungle.

CHAPTER 11

Skill 3—Organizing Space, Process Flow, and Feng Shui

To have a clear mind, it helps to have a clear living space. Hence the expression *to put one's house in order.* This idea dates back to ancient China and the practice of feng shui. As discussed in Part 2, the Three Steps to Optimal Health, Healing, and Longevity focus on optimizing your body, mind, and spirit; feng shui focuses on optimizing the peace, tranquility, and overall conduciveness to health and wellness of your external environment. Therefore, if you are going to focus on optimizing the health of your body, mind, and spirit, you should pay just as much attention to optimizing the contributory effects of your external environment. The two will support each other. In turn, this will facilitate time management, timely and effective communication, mental cognition, the creativity of your inner genius, the expression of passions and a winning attitude, and your ability to manage the direction and success of your life in general.

Optimizing your external environment will take time to think through, plan, and physically design. Naturally, your home space and workspace must be approached separately. Just as you manage your body, mind, and spirit to keep a clear mind that is ready to react and process matters on demand, you need to manage the activity in your physical space to keep it clear and ready to support the processing of your actions on demand. Regarding your workspace, this means defining your critical success factors, level of importance and urgency of your tasks, and applying the principals of time management as discussed in Chapter 9. Once this is done, you can effectively design your workspace—including your in-trays, files, storage cabinets, and desk—to best accommodate the successful management and completion of tasks. This requires planning and applying logistics to keep documents moving and to prevent dead ends and the over-accumulation of needless information. The same logic needs to be applied to the structure of your computer files, cell phone files, emails, and texts.

After completing the logistical aspect of organizing your space, it may help to consider the ancient wisdom of feng shui for a deeper level of organization and support. Feng shui has been practiced since the advent of agriculture and farming in China and dates back to 7500 BC. Although much of it appears to be common sense, an aspect of it relates to astrological data. Feng shui is highly regarded in architectural design in China and was most recently exemplified in the construction of the Bank of

China Tower in Hong Kong, which was so effectively designed to give the company a competitive edge that other buildings had to change elements of their design to compensate. Having applied feng shui in my own life, I can attest to its relevance and suggest that you consider using it to ensure that you survive and excel in the corporate jungle. This chapter will first discuss ways to logistically design your workspace for optimal workflow and productivity. I will then describe how you can further enhance your workspace with some basic feng shui principles. This will give you a sharper edge in your job performance and help you to stay happy, healthy, and successful in the corporate jungle.

Logistically Designing Workspace for Process Flow

The objective of designing your workspace should be to logistically support the efficiency and effectiveness of process flow to successfully perform your job. This may take a couple days or more to analyze and plan. However, doing so will be well worth it and will pay big dividends repeatedly for years to come.

To begin, think about your critical success factors and how to best support them. Thus, the process is closely related to (and supportive of) time management as discussed in Chapter 9. The next step is to identify and list the types of communication and documents delivered to you daily. For example, in my office, I receive documents and communications through the US Postal Service (USPS), private carriers, email, fax, and social media. Through the USPS, I receive professional journals, checks, direct-mail marketing with invitations to conferences, invitations to take out loans and apply for credit cards, payments for patient services, requests for information for insurance claims, notices to renew licenses, certificates, insurance, medical supplies for my office, and bills. Through private couriers, I receive mostly medical supplies and payroll checks. Through email, I receive personal messages, inquiries from new prospective patients, notices regarding insurance payments, notices regarding medical supply orders, notices regarding credit card payments, invitations to events and online seminars, notices from the bank, and miscellaneous junk. Through the telephone, I receive inquiries from prospective new patients, telemarketers, patient inquiries, and insurance company follow ups. Through social media, I receive messages from prospective new patients and marketers, useful medical information, results of studies, and news. All of these communications can be categorized by level of urgency, importance, and critical success factors discussed in Chapter 9 as follows:

     I.   New appointments

     II.   Patient care

     III.   Maintaining medical supply inventory

     IV.   Billing and collections

     V.   Administrative tasks

After identifying all categories and sources of information as above, you should make a table and assign a critical success factor, level of urgency/importance, and an action item for each. See the following examples.

US Postal Service

Information	Critical Success Factor	Importance/ Urgency	What to Do with It
Professional journals	I., II.	Important/ Not Urgent	Put in brief case to read at night or on weekends If not read in a month put in trash
Direct mail marketing	Various	Not Urgent/ Not Important	Quickly scan and put in trash if irrelevant If relevant, put in in-tray to think about If not acted upon in a timely manner, put in trash
Invitations to professional events and conferences	I., II.	Important/ Not Urgent	Quickly scan and put in trash if irrelevant If relevant, put in in-tray to think about If not acted upon in a timely

Information	Critical Success Factor	Importance/ Urgency	What to Do with It
			manner, put in trash
Checks for payments	IV.	Important/ Not Urgent	Place in a specific drawer and deposit ASAP
			Post all relevant information filed in drawer to accounting system weekly
			After posting, file in a special file for reference
			Three years of records kept on file; after that info can be archived or destroyed
Loans and line of credit offers	Various	Various	Scanned but mostly destroyed and put in trash
Credit card offers	Various	Various	Scanned but mostly destroyed and put in trash

Information	Critical Success Factor	Importance/ Urgency	What to Do with It
Third-party payer information requests	IV.	Important/ Urgent	Process weekly to facilitate collection
License renewals	I., II.	Important/ Not Urgent	Place in in-tray and process ahead of time when convenient
Insurance renewals	I., II.	Important/ Not Urgent	Place in in-tray and process ahead of time when convenient
Certificate renewals	I., II.	Important/ Not Urgent	Place in in-tray and process ahead of time when convenient
Bills	V.	Important/ Not Urgent	Place in in-tray and process ahead of time when convenient
Medical supplies	II., III.	Important/ Not Urgent	Open and store appropriately the same day

Private Couriers

Information	Critical Success Factor	Importance/ Urgency	What to Do with It
Medical supplies	II., III.	Important/ Not Urgent	Open and store appropriately the same day
Payroll checks	IV.	Important/ Not Urgent	Open and distribute the same day

Email

Information	Critical Success Factor	Importance/ Urgency	What to Do with It
Personal messages	None	Various	Scan and read; send replies discreetly, time permitting If a "thank you," save in testimonials file
Inquiries from new prospective patients	I.	Important/ Urgent	Reply immediately

Information	Critical Success Factor	Importance/ Urgency	What to Do with It
Notices regarding insurance payments	IV.	Important/ Urgent	Reply ASAP
Notices regarding medical supply orders	II., IV.	Important/ Not Urgent	Usually no response required
Notices regarding credit card receipts	IV.	Important/ Not Urgent	Usually duplicate information; no response needed
Invitations to events and online seminars	I., II.	Important/ Not Urgent	Quickly scan and put in trash if irrelevant If relevant, put in in-tray to think about If not acted upon in a timely manner, put in trash
Notices from the bank	IV., V.	Important/ Not Urgent	Usually duplicate information; no response necessary

Information	Critical Success Factor	Importance/ Urgency	What to Do with It
Miscellaneous junk	Various	Various	Quickly scan and delete as appropriate Unsubscribe from annoying sites or mark as junk/spam

Telephone

Information	Critical Success Factor	Importance/ Urgency	What to Do with It
Inquiries for prospective new patients	I., II.	Important/ Urgent	Reply immediately
Telemarketers	Various (mostly none)	Various	Usually irrelevant; remind that we are a no-call number and ask to be taken off the list
Patient inquiries	I., II.	Important/ Urgent	Respond immediately

Information	Critical Success Factor	Importance/ Urgency	What to Do with It
Insurance company follow-ups	IV.	Important/ Urgent	Respond ASAP

Social Media

Information	Critical Success Factor	Importance/ Urgency	What to Do with It
Prospective new patients	I., II.	Important/ Urgent	Respond immediately
Marketers	Various (mostly none)	Various	Scan and usually ignore
Useful medical information and study results	I., II., III.	Important/ Not Urgent	Scan and know where to find if future reference is necessary
News	Various (mostly none)	Various	Scan and usually ignore

In addition to documents delivered, it is important to consider all internally generated documents and items, including (in my case) patient records, the office schedule, cash receipts, credit card receipts, trash, and medical waste. All of these must be analyzed and an appropriate process flow designed to keep things moving for optimal efficiency. Ultimately, the goal is to avoid storing things temporarily—and then allowing them to stagnate—as this leads to inefficiency, confusion, and possibly to important information being lost. Ineffective process flow inhibits your ability to excel in the corporate jungle.

Once you identify all information and related documents, you should consider how to keep your documents and information organized and readily accessible as needed, in a systematic, ongoing basis. You should define the documents and information that you need the most to properly and effectively do your job. You should then take inventory and document the available space you have, along with available files and storage areas. As things arrive in your in-box, you need to keep them flowing by filing, tossing, or processing them. Therefore, you need a logical "next" place to put things to keep the in-box clear. An old expression I have heard repeatedly is to *never look at a piece of paper twice*. As mail and documents arrive in your in-box, you should move them along by immediately deciding if they are things you can simply file for your records—such as an invoice you know has been received and paid. Your files should be set up so that you can file such things readily in the moment and avoid using temporary storage or filing spots. This saves time and space, while maintaining clarity in your work environment, which also contributes to clarity in your mind.

However, items often need further processing. In those situations, you should decide if you can do it yourself or delegate it. If you are going to do it yourself, you should file it temporarily with similar documents, add it to your to-do list, prioritize it, and process it accordingly. If it is something you should delegate, send it along as quickly as possible so the next person can process it.

You may look at a document or piece of mail and decide it is something you will not need in the near future, if ever. If that is the case, you should toss it in the trash immediately. Too often, we think we will use or refer to something in the future and waste precious space and time filing and storing it only to discover months or even years later that you never looked at it again. You then waste more time examining it and finally throw it in the trash. Try to remember: *never look at a piece of paper twice.* In most cases, you can easily find any information contained in such documents on the Internet quicker than you could find it in your files. When in doubt, throw it out.

To better assess your need for storage trays, bins, and files, you should write down and document your daily, weekly, and monthly processes and the documentation needed to support them. Next, assess whether you have appropriate space and storage devices to store or keep things flowing in a neat, organized, and timely fashion. You may need to order something new. The key to remember is to figure out what works for you. Go online or visit your local office supply store to get ideas and make things happen. This is one area where it is not recommended to skimp on the budget. You need equipment that is easy to use and that will last for years to come. Before buying anything, make a thorough list of the types of documents and paperwork you receive in a given period, assess the volume of such documents, and what you must do with it after you receive it. Some items are for the trash, some are for immediate filing, some require periodic processing on deadlines, some are passed to others for processing, and still others require periodic processing with less urgency (and perhaps no defined deadline).

Once you define the incoming documents, you can decide what types of *collection bins* you will need to quickly put things in order and promote timely processing. You may find the first thing you need is a bigger wastebasket. Next, you will most likely need an adequate file draw or file cabinet to store the items and records you will readily need. You should define this file's size according to the volume of these items and records given the nature of your job. There is no sense taking up valuable space with an oversized file cabinet; having one may prompt you to store unnecessary documents. On the other hand, you do not want a storage drawer that is inadequate causing you to leave your desk a mess. For documents with a deadline that require periodic processing, you will want an open in-box, which gives you a constant visual awareness of the quantity of such work. This also helps you to better plan your to-do list and thereby manage your time. The same thinking applies to other documents. The key is to have storage trays that collect documents by category, letting you systematically access and process them without losing or overlooking anything. In addition, these collection places should be esthetically appealing; this will help you not only *be* more organized, but also *feel* more organized.

You should apply the same principles used for paper documents to files stored on your computer, email, voicemail, and so on. It goes without saying that a computer with files neatly organized and easily accessible will offer more peace of mind and productivity than one with files stored randomly. Being able to efficiently access and process information on timely basis not only increases your performance, but it will make you feel more efficient and organized. This will minimize stress levels and promote a calm and focused mind. This in turn will promote health and will ensure that you will not only survive in the corporate jungle, but also excel.

Basics of Feng Shui

After logistically designing your workspace for optimal process flow, information storage, and timely task completion, you might want to enhance your environment with some feng shui basics. One of the most fundamental principles of feng shui is to avoid having a cluttered environment. By following the tips above to logistically design your space, you should have removed any clutter and therefore be ready to take advantage of other, more extensive feng shui principles. Keep in mind that there are different methodologies behind feng shui, and some are more complex than others. The most complex and comprehensive approach to feng shui is the traditional Chinese method. To apply the traditional Chinese method of feng shui, you need to know the year your building was completely constructed. This is defined as the year the roof was completed. Further, you must analyze the direction that the building faces. This is usually the direction that the front door opens to, but can be complex with modern architecture and odd-shaped buildings. Once you have determined this information, you can look up the astrological aspects of the building and implement them into the design and layout of internal furnishings. The most important information you can gain here is how conducive your building is to producing health and wealth; some buildings are conducive to both or just one of these aspects, while others are conducive to neither. It should be noted that some buildings are simply "unlucky." You probably know of a few business locations or even houses where the occupants change frequently. Most likely, these are unlucky buildings. Although there are some books on these aspects of feng shui and you may be able to look up this information on your own, you can also hire a feng shui professional. Every building can be divided into nine quadrants with each quadrant given a separate evaluation regarding its conduciveness to promoting health and wealth. The objective is to maximize all positive aspects and minimize negative aspects with the use of decorations, objects of nature, and furniture layout to promote health and wealth.

The challenge with the traditional Chinese method is that it is complex and may not be practical to apply. However, if you feel your structure is unlucky or disharmonious based on continuous health problems, constant hidden expenses, or bad luck that continues to drain finances, you may wish to hire a feng shui professional to determine if the situation is salvageable and what you can do about it. If the cost of correcting it is prohibitive, you may have difficulty explaining that to your boss or spouse. Meanwhile, you might try applying the simpler Tibetan method and observe the results. During my tenure studying feng shui, my professor said that feng shui comprises about 25 percent of the energy in our lives and that our inner intentions, lifestyle, and diet account for the remaining 75 percent. For this reason, I prefer to use the Tibetan method of feng shui as it is simple, practical, and economical. Even if this method is only half as effective as the traditional Chinese method, we are still getting half, or 12.5 percent, of the benefits available from feng shui. You can maximize the rest with good intentions, healthy lifestyle, and a regulated diet as discussed throughout this book.

The Tibetan method assigns energetic aspects of a room or building based on the position of the main entrance. See Figure 11.1 below. Accordingly, the corner furthest to the left upon entering any room or building possesses the room's energy for wealth potential, the corner furthest to the right possesses the room's potential for developing intimate relationships, the corner closest to the right represents the energy potential for encouraging help from colleagues, friends, and family, and the corner closest to the left contains the room's potential for helping us gain and make use of our knowledge. In addition to each corner's energetic qualities, the center of the room represents our overall health and well-being. The position between the knowledge corner and the wealth corner contains the room's energetic potential to assist us with the strength of our family life. The position between the wealth corner and the intimate relationship corner represents the energetic potential for promoting our reputations. The position between the relationships corner and the helpful people corner represents the room's energetic potential to promote offspring. Finally, the space between the helpful people corner and the knowledge corner contains the energetic potential of developing and maintaining a clear career path and purpose in life.

Figure 11.1 The Tibetan method energetic aspects of a room or building based on the position of the main entrance.

Wealth Potential, Good Fortune, Abundance	Fame and Reputation	Intimate Relationships, Love, Marriage
Harmony with Family	Overall Health and Well-being	Potential for Procreation, Well-being of Offspring
Knowledge, Wisdom, and Intuition	Career, Life's Purpose	Helpful Family, Friends, and Colleagues

Main Entrance

The overall objective here is to decide which of these energetic aspects are most important to you and to avoid cluttering these areas. Instead you should focus on keeping these spaces open to enhance energy flow. Things that may inhibit energy flow are plants (especially decorative dried plants) and clutter.

Things that enhance energy flow are crystals, moving water (such as in fountains or aquariums), burning candles, and wind chimes. For example, if you are mostly concerned with accumulating wealth, then you should make sure not to crowd that corner of the room with clutter, to keep it an open space, and to decorate it with a crystal, fountain, aquarium, a candle, or a wind chime.

The Tibetan method emphasizes a few other underlying principles. One of the most important fundamentals is the position of your desk or bed. The emphasis is to have your desk or bed positioned as much as possible in the center of the room while facing all entrances and windows. You should not only avoid having your back to any entrance, but also avoid having your back to a window as well. Further, you should avoid having your desk or bed in the direct pathway of any entrance or doorway. See Figure 11.2 below.

Given space restrictions, following these guidelines may not be practical or possible. In that case, you should do the best you can. You might need to make compromises when economics and practicality present limitations.

Once the positioning of your desk or bed is settled, you should consider the positioning of all other items, paying attention to different energetic aspects of the room. Although you may feel the need to decorate all corners and space of the room, you should think practically. In terms of your office or workspace, you may not want to stick too far out from the norm of your company and colleagues, as this can go against the political current (see the discussion on communication in Chapter 10).

Figure 11.2 The Tibetan method emphasizes positioning your desk or bed as much as possible in the center of the room while facing all entrances and windows.

Window	
Not such a good place for bed or desk, as you are in the direct path of the door/entrance.	A good place for bed or desk, as you can see the window and door in your field of vision. Avoid having your back to the door or window if possible. Not such a good place for bed or desk, as the door/entrance is not in your field of vision

Main Entrance

Although the benefits of clearing clutter and organizing documents and workflow are inarguable, feng shui may not be for everybody. However, my attitude is that it has been successfully practiced for so long in the Far East that there must be something to it. Unless it goes against the political current of your organization, it is not going to hurt and will only add more creatively to your office's ambiance. In fact, I must admit that since learning about feng shui some 20 years ago, I recently reviewed my income and found that I made the most money and was the happiest and most successful during the years that I applied focused feng shui principles to my house and office. I also remember a year in which I shared an office with someone who had a habit of accumulating clutter anywhere possible; that year, my income was a disaster, and I also experienced health problems that I never had before and have never had since. One lesson I learned from that experience was to never mess with bad feng shui. And again, to survive in the corporate jungle, we need to gain every edge we can. So, why not be on the current edge by enhancing our Western world with some Eastern wisdom? You can easily achieve this in a subtle fashion that does not stick out. For anyone who is doubtful about the effects of feng shui, I challenge you to implement some of the principles and make a judgment for yourself as to its effectiveness.

Summary

After logistically designing and engineering your workspace for optimal process flow, clearing out clutter, and applying some feng shui principles, you may find that your office or home feels like a whole new place. This should give you a strong sense of focus and make you feel more grounded, centered, and calm. You should also see your productivity and energy level surge. Do not take this for granted and allow clutter and disorganization to reappear; instead, schedule periodic organizing sessions. You may even want to take a day or so to reorganize if your job requirements change, as you may need to reevaluate and redesign all over again. A clear and effective environment will support a clear and effective mind, which will help you stay healthy and excel in the corporate jungle.

CHAPTER 12

Skill 4—Developing Cognitive Skills and Cultivating Your Genius

Have you ever been stumped for words in a meeting or during an interview, only to figure out what you should have said later, when it's too late? Have you ever simply forgotten to do an important task? Have you ever come up with a great money-making idea and done nothing about it, only to find out later than someone else made a fortune from the same idea? These are some situations that can be avoided with strongly developed cognitive skills and a cultivated inner genius.

Cognitive skills and your inner genius go hand in hand. You cannot truly benefit from one without the other. While cognitive skills include the process of absorbing information, processing it, and applying it, your inner genius represents both your capacity to exercise your cognitive skills and to actually produce or create a concept. This could be an idea or something physical, such as an invention. Strong cognitive skills will allow you to cultivate and express your inner genius. Without applying your cognitive skills, it is difficult to harness your inner genius to create anything tangible. However, having strong cognitive skills alone does not automatically cultivate a significant level of genius; you must apply your skills and create tangible results. Both areas take practice to develop. Cognitive skills and your level of genius may vary throughout your life and can be influenced by many variables, but both faculties play a major role in staying healthy and succeeding in the corporate jungle. This chapter will discuss the synergies of cognitive skills and your inner genius, how cognitive skills are developed, and how your inner genius can be cultivated and developed. In addition, I will review some established techniques for ongoing maintenance of cognitive skills, continuous cultivation of your inner genius, and how both faculties can benefit your personal and professional life.

Cognitive Skills and Your Inner Genius

Most everyone has at some time in their life taken an IQ test. An IQ test score is a general indication of your cognitive ability. Many people are under the impression that we are born with a fixed IQ that is defined genetically, and that we are either a genius or not based upon an IQ test. However, your IQ score is merely a general indication of your cognitive ability at the time of the exam, and it is only one aspect of your inner genius. Research shows that this is not necessarily an indication of your ability to succeed in life. While some people with the highest IQ scores do not achieve much in their lifetimes, others who do not score so high on these exams may excel in all endeavors. Accordingly, your IQ or cognitive ability needs to be applied and combined with your inner genius to allow for creations and achievements that lead to your success.

Your cognitive ability, formal education, work experience, life experiences, personal working knowledge base, and your accomplishments are all part of your inner genius. Therefore, your inner genius can change over time. With use and by applying these collective parts in a positive environment, your genius can increase. Similarly, lack of use and a negative environment can lead your genius to decline. Because most corporate careers do not require much physical activity and solely revolve around mental activities, the development, application, and maintenance of your inner genius is key to your health and success in the corporate jungle. Even if you believe your job does not require you to be a genius, it is important that you do not allow your genius to decline as it is part of your inner *human resources department* (see Chapter 14). Just as you might exercise and go to the gym to maintain physical strength and abilities—regardless of whether you need them for your job or not—it is important to participate in activities that strengthen and maintain your cognition and inner genius. Both are key aspects of optimal health, longevity, and your ability to excel in all endeavors.

Developing Cognitive Skills

Cognitive skills are developed in four primary areas:

1. Family life

2. Formal education

3. Work experiences

4. Life experiences

All of these areas contribute to increasing your personal working knowledge base. Your inner genius can then apply this knowledge, which leads to accomplishments. These accomplishments then add even more to your working knowledge base, and the cycle continues. This cumulative process can lead to greater cognition, genius, and accomplishments throughout your life. The process can be immensely rewarding and meaningful.

Family life during childhood is the first place where cognitive skills can be developed. This is usually done with parents, siblings, and close friends through educational games and toys, visits to the zoo and museums, and playing sports. These early years are also a time when many learn musical instruments and foreign languages. The following six aspects of cognition can be developed in family life:

1. Focus

2. Memory

3. Analytical thinking

4. Making comparisons

5. Self-expression

6. Motor skills

Some of the key analytical skills that can be developed are evaluating, making comparisons, and understanding cause and effect. Although many of these aspects of cognition are first developed in early family life, it is never too late to continue to sharpen and develop such skills during adulthood.

Formal education builds on these cognitive skills and helps us develop skills in three other key areas:

1. Critical thinking

2. Adaptability

3. Knowledge in academic domains

Critical thinking skills are the foundation from which you apply your genius through in-depth analysis of data and applications of logic to make sound decisions and conclusions. Adaptive skills include developing social skills needed both for strong societal bonding and cohesiveness in group efforts. Finally, building academic knowledge through formal education helps to build a strong foundation or expertise in a field in order to launch a career. Most of us will have obtained our formal education in the earlier part of our lives, but it is increasingly popular to continue with formal educational programs later in life, as well.

Work and life experiences also offer a variety of rich opportunities to further apply and develop all the above cognitive skills. Through these applications of cognitive skills, we have the opportunity to cultivate our inner genius.

Cultivating Your Inner Genius

Work and life experiences offer ideal environments for applying and cultivating your inner genius. After sufficiently developing your cognitive skills and developing some expertise in a field, your work and life experiences will continuously provide opportunities to apply all you have learned and enhance the cultivation of your inner genius. You do this through constant exposure to unpredictable situations that need resolution. The work environment will give you challenges that let you apply critical thinking, be compensated for your accomplishments, and contribute to society. Being successful in the workplace can build your inner confidence, increase your passion for further developing your related knowledge base, and inspire a strong desire to further cultivate your inner genius.

Life experiences are much like work experiences, except they are more socially related. Examples include raising a family, traveling and living abroad, and participating in sports, groups, and clubs. Like work experiences, life experiences will also continue to add to your accomplishments, expertise in life, and inner knowledge base, and will further enhance cognition and your inner genius.

In addition to strategically planning your career, you should do your best to have as many diverse life experiences as possible. Reading, traveling, learning a new language, and playing a musical instrument are all rich experiences that offer diverse methods for cognitive development. Your ongoing family life, formal education, work experiences, and life experiences will continue to construct your working knowledge base and offer opportunities to exercise and strengthen cognitive skills and cultivate your inner genius. As you continue this cycle, it will offer a rich, meaningful, and rewarding life.

Self-Analysis of Cognitive Skills and Applied Inner Genius

You may wish to take a moment and trace how your cognitive skills were developed and how you have applied your inner genius. This exercise can highlight aspects of your life that you have taken for granted and can increase your gratitude for all that you have. It may also highlight some voids and remind you of unused potential. This could encourage you to take that next step to grow and develop. You may decide that you need additional formal education or training to fulfill your strategic plan or life's mission (see Chapter 14). Perhaps you will decide that you need more hands-on application of knowledge, such as that gained through an internship or additional work experience. Some of you may decide to travel abroad. This process will further enhance your inner genius. Remember, it is never too late to grow and develop.

My Personal Journey

In looking back at my own experiences, I am forever grateful for parents who emphasized educational toys and games during early childhood. They also encouraged reading, visits to museums, informal education in Boy Scouts, and participation in sports. Further, their ultimate emphasis was on formal education. With an undergraduate degree in business management and a graduate degree in medicine, my formal education has set a firm knowledge base for me to launch two careers. In turn, my business degree and knowledge base as an experienced Certified Public Accountant allowed me to work globally with Deloitte & Touche. Working and living internationally further enhanced my knowledge base of human social psychology, both within and outside of the workplace. This allowed my mind to expand further, through adopting different cultures and lifestyles. In doing so, I came to realize that there are many ways and manners in which to approach life. This led me to realize that I did not have to stay with one career, as is the societal norm; and this realization, in turn, gave me the courage to pursue my passion. As a result, I chose to study Traditional Chinese Medicine. When I began this study of medicine, I thought I was leaving my corporate knowledge and experience behind. Instead, with an expertise in two fields, my inner genius began to combine the two experiences, which resulted in my creating this book, which in turn will create new opportunities to grow. Overall, I must give equal credit to all my experiences collectively in developing my cognitive skills, cultivating my inner genius, and creating the opportunity to continuously build my working knowledge base. Given my own experience, I encourage everyone to embrace as many opportunities as possible to continuously strengthen their cognitive skills, cultivate their inner genius, build their inner knowledge base, and continue to grow and advance in their career and life.

Techniques for Maintaining Cognitive Skills and Continuously Cultivating Your Inner Genius

As emphasized above, the strength of your cognitive skills and the potential of your genius can vary throughout your life. Like physical strength, without the proper exercises and environment, both can become weak. Because both are essential to our success in life, they must continuously be used and strengthened. Sharp and fully functioning cognitive skills are vital to staying healthy and excelling in the corporate jungle. You might have the highest IQ, a rich bank of life experiences, and the highest of educational degrees, but without adequately maintained and applied cognitive skills, all can be lost regarding the inner genius. Below is a discussion of cognitive skills, how you can develop them, and how you can combine them with your inner genius for a healthy, successful, and rewarding life.

Combining your cognitive skills with your inner genius allows you to do the following:

1. Absorb information

2. Process it

3. Apply it in your actions and decision-making

4. Accomplish goals and create desired outcomes

Here, we will discuss how you can develop and enhance these skills. We will also discuss how you can apply them to optimize your health and success.

To develop and enhance your ability to absorb information, you should start with a relaxed mind, as a relaxed state allows your memory to function optimally. The best way to maintain a relaxed mind is to practice the Three Steps to Optimal Health, Healing, and Longevity, as discussed in Part 2. In addition to a relaxed mind, it is also important to understand the impact of the medium through which information is delivered. If you are using video, then good vision and auditory skills are essential for absorption. If you are accessing information via a computer and/or the Internet, strong technical skills may be needed. If information is delivered by recordings, podcasts, and so on, then auditory skills need to be developed and maintained. If information is transferred in a classroom, you may need to develop note-taking skills, as you cannot control the speed of delivery. Additionally, in a classroom, you might need interpersonal skills to best interact with instructors and students. These factors must be considered when developing cognitive skills and your inner genius. Further, some people innately absorb information more effectively through one delivery medium than through others. For example, some people are more visual than auditory, and vice versa. A classic example of this is Albert Einstein: he did not do so well academically in high school, where the learning environment was strict, highly structured, and regimented. Overall, you will not always have the opportunity to choose your delivery medium, so it is important to make the best of whatever medium is available.

Once important information is presented, we must commit it to memory. Common examples of this type of workplace information include names, schedules, itineraries, and technical information; having rote access to such information lets your creativity continue working and avoids the tiring tedium of having to constantly look things up. To absorb information, it is important to devise effective ways to memorize it. Following are some memorization techniques (listed from most to least effective) and the situations in which they are most applicable.

Technique	How to do it	Where applicable
Self-Testing	Create flashcards (digital or non-digital). Make a list of keywords and quiz yourself on their meaning.	Almost all situations
Distributed Practice	Do not try to absorb and memorize everything at once; instead, spread	Almost all situations

Technique	How to do it	Where applicable
	absorption and memorizing over planned time periods.	
Elaborative Interrogation	Analyze and elaborate on information to be absorbed by asking a series of "why" questions pertaining to facts. For example: Why is this information important? Why will I need it? Why does it make sense?	Technical information
Self-Explanation	Similar to elaborate interrogation, but now you can ask any question you want, which lets you further analyze and elaborate on information you wish to absorb.	Technical information

Technique	How to do it	Where applicable
	Example questions might include: How is this information important to my job? What situations will I apply it in?	

There are many ways to further enhance cognitive skills. First, you can apply and enhance your cognition through reading, crossword puzzles, social interaction, computer programs, video games designed for this purpose, and physical exercise. Although all of these have proven effective in developing and training cognitive skills, it should be noted that exercise is the best. Although all exercise is beneficial, studies have shown that doing 30 minutes of strenuous exercise (where you become out of breath) twice a week is the best way to enhance cognitive skills.

With strongly developed cognitive skills, you will be able to readily absorb information. Information absorption and retention is the first cognitive skill essential to building a knowledge base for the inner genius to work with. Once absorbed, the developed genius must be able to process information, apply it, and use it for actions and decision-making. This is where the inner genius can provide insights and creativity for decision-making and accomplishments.

There are two basic methods of processing absorbed knowledge for this purpose:

1. Make logical use of absorbed knowledge by analyzing it, then using a deliberate, methodical trial-and-error exploration to arrive at solutions.

2. Allow the subconscious to creatively incubate absorbed knowledge to encourage creative insights and breakthroughs that offer solutions toward a focused subject.

Both applications are useful, however, it is the second method—using creative incubation—that brings about the most creative solutions. This method has five basic stages:

1. Preparation

2. Incubation

3. Insight

4. Verification

5. Follow-through

Preparation is the process of absorbing information. As discussed above, we achieve preparation through family upbringing, formal education and training, work experience, and life experiences. The ultimate level of absorbing information is to attain the level of an expert in a certain field. Once you have attained this expertise, you can then apply your inner genius to solve problems creatively. Psychologists agree that the best way to do this is to first analyze all the facts and variables of a situation, and then attempt to find a solution through analysis. You can do mental exercises to trigger abstract correlations; example exercises include doing puzzles or looking at an object, such as a paper clip, as if it were a piece of wire and imagining different uses for it. In addition, it is recommended to quiet your mind and let your subconscious work subliminally. This is called the *incubation stage*.

One of the best ways of incubating an idea is through meditation. Other ways to incubate ideas are through exercise, taking a walk, qi gong, yoga, or simply taking a nap and sleeping on it. Studies and history show that many of the greatest ideas come to people while they are daydreaming, taking a shower, driving to work, or simply doing something unrelated and thereby relaxing and allowing their imagination and creative forces to be most effective. Also, your imagination and creative forces are stronger when you follow the Three Steps to Optimal Health, Healing, and Longevity as discussed in Part 2.

Following incubation, we hope for the big *aha moment* of insight and idea creation; this occurs in the *insight stage*. In this stage, many people experience excitement, wonderment, positive energy, and conviction. However, many people become so excited and intellectually satisfied in the insight stage, that they lose the focus and ambition necessary to reach the *verification and follow-through stages*. However, it is only in the follow-through phase that our insight or idea can be verified and validated.

It is thus vital to harness positive energy (see Chapter 15) and focus it on these verification and follow-through stages. It is in these stages that the breakthrough can be shared and interpreted collectively for practicality, validation, or creative enhancements. Although, in these stages, we run the risk of the idea becoming a failure, it helps to remember that many great inventors created many more failing ideas than successful ideas.

You should not allow that to stop you from the possible reward of a successful creation. Successful creations make not only the creator happy, but also those who benefit from the creation. To experience a level of true creative genius, you must not give up. Even producing an idea that fails can bring many moments of joy and spark new interests in our lives. Further, you can use this creative force called *genius* as a form of daily quiet time (see Chapter 6) and can further enhance it by cultivating your passion (see Chapter 13). Therefore, your creative genius and the associated cognitive skills can be applied in both your personal and professional lives. The rewards can be endless. I therefore strongly emphasize developing your mental cognition and inner genius as a key aspect of maintaining optimal health while excelling in a corporate environment.

Summary

It is important to be able to say what you want at the right times. It is also essential to keep the important tasks in mind and take your ideas to fruition. Developed cognitive skills and a cultivated inner genius will help in these areas. Cognitive skills and your inner genius go hand in hand. You cannot have one without the other. Developing both starts in your childhood years, but both can and should be maintained and developed throughout your life. You can do this through your family life, formal education, work experience, life experience, and by applying your skills and genius to create or achieve something. Cognitive skills and expressing your inner genius are essential to success in a corporate environment, and therefore must be constantly strengthened, developed, and applied. There are several ways of doing this. In addition to programs that might be offered at work, you should design and participate in your own programs to stay cognitively sharp and apply your creative inner genius. This will make your life more rewarding, healthier, happier, and make you more successful in the corporate jungle and elsewhere.

CHAPTER 13

Skill 5—Cultivating Passion

Passion is a very powerful aspect of being human. In Chapter 7, we discussed how doing things you are passionate about can be a great form of daily quiet time. When you do something you are passionate about, it relaxes your CNS and can bring you out of a fight-or-flight response and return you to the state of optimal health, healing, and longevity.

In Chapter 12, we discussed passion as a key element in giving you the drive to develop and apply your inner genius. If passion can do all this, imagine what it can do if applied to your professional life. We tend to enjoy what we are doing more, do things better, put up with more crap, and give more effort when we are driven by passion. Therefore, we should all try to find jobs that we are passionate about. This may seem like a novelty to some, but the opportunity to change your career has never been easier than in our developed world today. There is no doubt that passion is a key element that will help ensure your success in the corporate jungle. The difficulty is first discovering what you are passionate about. But exactly what is passion? How do we find our own inner passion? Once you find it, how do you use passion to reap its benefits? In this chapter, we will discuss the concept of passion, its benefits, how to find your own, and how to have the confidence to pursue it.

The word *passion* has many implications. Overall, passion implies intense emotions, feelings with drive, or a zealous enthusiasm or desire for something. Many times, passionate feelings and emotions override logic and may be based on instinct. The word *passion* comes from the Latin word *patior*, meaning to suffer or to endure. This implies that when we have a passion for something, we are willing to possibly suffer and endure whatever it takes to attain it. Passion can be in the form of an intense emotion—such as excitement or enthusiasm—applied to a subject, idea, person, or object. A person is said to have a passion for something when they have a strong positive affinity for it. A love for something and a passion for something are very similar feelings.

Considering the above, you can imagine the positive effects on your CNS that a career with passion can have versus one without passion. No doubt, a career without passion can become tedious, boring, and stressful, causing you to go into a state of fight-or-flight whenever you are at work or even thinking about work. Correspondingly, a career with passion— while no less demanding—can fill you with hope and inspiration while at work or thinking about it. The career without passion will lead to more sickness and poor health and decrease your chances of succeeding, while the career with passion will lead to a healthier more invigorating life with a greater chance of not only surviving, but excelling in the corporate jungle.

The importance of passion in your career is not a new concept. However, it seems that many of us chose our careers and jobs in a somewhat random manner. From random decision-making, you can expect only random results: sometimes we get lucky, but often we are disappointed and can waste a lot of time and effort on a career path that simply lacks our passion. How passionate are you about your career? Do you dread Monday morning? Are you always counting the days of the week? If so, you may greatly benefit from a career with more passion.

The benefits of a career with passion are emphasized in the ancient Hindu concept of *dharma*, which says that when one is doing what one is meant to do in life, the universe will always provide; not too much, but not too little. Another concept, this from the ancient philosophy of Taoism, says that those things we do with passion express our treasures of the heart or our gifts at birth. It is said that if you pay tribute to your treasures, the universe will pay tribute back by presenting situations, people, events, and circumstances (SPECs) that will light your path and show you the way to a healthy, happy, and successful life. According to these ancient concepts, it could be said that, by following your passion, it is your destiny to succeed and that success comes easier for those who follow their passion.

The opposite is true if you are not following your passion. Things become difficult to deal with, stressful, and success is ever so elusive. Needless to say, many of our problems in life can be eliminated if we follow our passion. Following your passion is like having a protective shield as you confront your trials and tribulations; not only does it make it easier to tolerate stressful events, it helps to eliminate them. So, if you think it may be difficult to find your passion and make a change, think of how much more difficult life may be if you do not. If you are in a difficult situation that will not allow you to change your career, it is not the end of the world—but it does make it that much more important that you express your passions in your daily quiet time, as discussed in Chapter 6.

Regarding your daily quiet time, when you are passionate about work, it is much easier to switch gears into your personal life when you get home. Too many times in my prior career, I became so mentally drained in a negative way at work that I did not have the energy to switch into the activities of my personal life after work. I became lazy, sometimes watching television instead of going to the gym, meditating, or doing something more constructive for myself. If work was stressful and draining it could affect my sleep and eventually lead to illness. Things are different in my current career with passion; even though my work can sometimes be draining—as I give much of myself to others—I feel rewarded because I am passionate about the healing process and thus am more motivated to do something for myself at the end of the day. Correspondingly, after taking part in a nourishing form of daily quiet time, I am more likely to sleep well and be ready for a productive day at work. For those with families, when you are passionate about work, you are more likely to quickly engage with your spouse and children and thereby cultivate more loving and meaningful relationships on an ongoing basis. A career and life with passion feeds itself with infinite positive energy, as discussed in Chapter 15.

Another great benefit of following your passion is that, when you approach retirement, you will be able to look back and feel like you contributed something to yourself, your family, and society. Without passion, many people end up retiring and wondering what they really did all their lives and why. Many have the feeling that although they did everything *right*, they never did anything for themselves. Therefore, they end up feeling like their lives were empty. This is not an ideal life. If passion is not part of your work, I highly recommend expressing it in your personal life.

Given all the benefits of having a career with passion, why do so few people feel passion toward their careers? This is largely because schools and parents tend to emphasize practical careers rather than passionate careers. Therefore, most of us are not taught to emphasize passion in formulating our career path. However, since most of us are not born with unlimited resources, practicality is something to keep in mind and to blend into your career with passion. So, how do you find a career that you are passionate about, that will also be practical and support a family or simply provide a comfortable lifestyle? My first recommendation is to ask yourself what you like to do. Next, ask yourself which of those passions offers you an opportunity to make a living. This requires sitting down and being very candid with yourself; it may also require research to determine the viability of making a living at each alternative. You must be honest with yourself and not be influenced by other people's opinions. Passions are like fingerprints; no two individual passions will be the same. Your passion might seem absurd to others. Therefore, trying to match your passion with what is acceptable to others could lead you to an absurd and unhealthy life. Be honest with yourself and open your heart to the field of all possibilities. You will not only unlock your passion, but also the door to a happier, healthier, and more rewarding life.

You must remember to commit to taking action toward your passion. In trying to find your passion, you should consider those types of activities that strike a chord in your heart. Although ideally, your passion is best expressed in your career, if that is not practically attainable any time soon, you can gain many benefits from hobbies and leisure activities that let you express your passion. After making the list of activities that strike a chord in your heart, you can start committing time in your schedule to participate in these activities. This is crucially important; too many people procrastinate and end up in a place of stagnation. From my experience, it is when we take the action that the magic happens. Call me a geek, but when I was in the corporate world, I became passionate about time management. This led me to the concept of using my time wisely and focusing on activities that I was passionate about. In turn, this led me to start meditating, which then led me to a calling to practice medicine. This list goes on and continues today. So, remember: once you identify those activities that you are passionate about, commit the time to participate in them, and watch the magic happen.

In pursuing your passion, you may meet with many obstacles and perceived barriers. When this happens, take a good look at what is holding you back. Just recently, I took a course on self-discovery, only to realize through it that, in being the fourth of six children growing up, I suffered from middle-child syndrome. As a middle child, I realized at an early age how easy it was to go unnoticed. Correspondingly, I began enjoying life *under the radar*. However, I subconsciously developed the negative attitude that no one cared and that I did not matter. As an adult, I came to realize that this underlying attitude sometimes makes me complacent when it comes to climbing outside of the box in pursuit of my passion. So, in pursuing your passion, it can be highly useful to get to know yourself. Become intimately familiar with your strengths and weaknesses, and make a list of them. Identify how your strengths can help you in your pursuit, but also be aware of how your weaknesses can slow you down and hold you back. Write out how you can overcome your weaknesses when this happens. It could mean the difference between a life of complacency and a life of wonder, living your dream!

Tapping into your faith or belief system is another great way of fueling yourself and giving yourself the strength and fortitude needed to pursue your passion. Most belief systems emphasize that we are all here on Earth for a purpose. Although most of us heard this at an early age, many of us ignore this concept. I remember when I first started to entertain the idea of pursuing my passion, I was living a life where I thought only people like da Vinci and Michelangelo pursued their passion and the rest of us just went to work.

However, slowly I began to shift in my outlook and decided that perhaps I too had a divine purpose. In pursuing my passion for meditation, I was invited to participate in a guidance-through-synchronicity project that required me to visualize a life of passion and look for SPECs or messages in my daily conversations, reading, and media exposure that seemed to offer hints as to my purpose in life. The project was two weeks long and, as it progressed, I began to realize that I was more suited for a healthcare profession. However, given my personal interests, it had to be something spiritual and holistic.

On the last evening of the project, I went to a yoga class and my instructor asked how the project was going and what conclusions I had reached. After sharing the above with her, she recommended acupuncture and Traditional Chinese Medicine. I remember thinking it was a stretch, but nonetheless, I wrote it in my journal as something to consider. As I was writing in my journal, I received a phone call from a close friend who said she had just been to the library and took out a video on Chinese medicine and healing with the mind. She further strongly emphasized that she thought I "would really like it!" Sure enough, after watching the video, I stated, "If I can make a living doing that, that's what I am doing," and here I am today. I really do believe that having two people, who did not know each other, independently suggest acupuncture as a career for me in one night—and doing so exactly at the conclusion of the project—is about as divine as it gets. This gave me the courage to leave my home in Boston and drive out to California without knowing a soul and make it happen. One positive thing after another occurred, as one door after another opened for me. I found the best jobs that paid the most money I had ever made, with the most flexibility; this let me attend medical school in a night and weekend program. I truly felt blessed in my path. And it is this blessing that keeps me going, even through adversity. Additionally, many blessings have followed that make me feel like I am on a divine path and making a contribution to the world and humanity. It is the feeling of being blessed that gives me the patience and persistence to stay focused on my career path.

It's been a little over 20 years since I changed careers, and I am now a passionate Doctor of Acupuncture. I can honestly say that my job has just as many challenges and opportunities for stress, but my passion for what I do allows me to forge ahead and reap the rewards of realizing my passion and my life's purpose. One of the most rewarding aspects is the act of writing this book, as I hope to make the corporate jungle a better and more compatible place for all human beings to express their passions and live rewarding lives. I feel like this book addresses some simple, fundamental concepts that, when applied, could generate a huge beneficial shift for the world. I now feel like I have a purpose in life much like da Vinci or Michelangelo. I do not simply *go to work* anymore. My passion has given me the courage and confidence to pursue and achieve my life's purpose. The point here is that, when pursuing your passion, do not hesitate to include your faith in the equation. It can make all the difference.

Summary

Passion is an intense feeling and rich with emotions that encompass your body, mind, and spirit. With some serious soul-searching and an independent mind, we can find our passion within our joy. It may be necessary to combine passion with practicality when applying your passion to your career. In any case, the most important thing is to take action by committing time to activities that encompass your passion. This, in turn, will create opportunities and SPECs to further express that passion. You must learn how to harness your strengths and conquer your weaknesses to take advantage of these opportunities. Finally, keep your faith in all your endeavors and do not underestimate the power of divine guidance. A life with passion is rich with healthy relationships and rewarding experiences.

From my experience, I recommend finding what you can best identify as your passion and going for it. Even if you are already successful, you may want to expand and pursue something else. This is particularly true if your life has not met your expectations; in that case, there is a good chance that pursuing your passion will open the doors to new ideas and new passions. Following your passion is a skill and, like any other skill, it needs to be developed throughout your lifetime. Many times, following your passion can be a trial-and-error process. However, I have never met anyone who ever regretted following their passion. Whether it is a hobby or a career, go for it!

CHAPTER 14

Skill 6—Adapting to Change and Managing Yourself

THAT'S PETERSON FROM ACCOUNTING... HE'S ADAPTING WELL.

As mentioned in Chapter 2, the one key element that most contributed to the survival of human beings over our Neanderthal and Homo erectus cousins is our *ability to adapt to change and develop the skills and tools necessary to help us further adapt to change.* This is evidenced by our ability to adapt to ice ages, disease, predators, and natural disasters, while developing tools and learning to farm. It is often said that the only thing constant in life is change. Living in the information age and the age of globalization, this principle has never been stronger in the corporate world. Therefore, developing your ability and skills to adapt to change is a concept most worthy of consideration. This chapter will discuss change and how it can affect our lives. It will also discuss what we can do to prepare for change, take action to adapt to change, and move forward successfully with good health.

A Half Century of Change

Our world, environment, job environment, families, and friends, and we ourselves are constantly changing. Considering improved transportation and telecommunications, our world is becoming smaller and smaller. I can keep in touch daily with friends I made while working globally almost 30 years ago. At the push of a button, I can speak to them and see their faces on a laptop or mobile phone, all for free. For a reasonable price, I can jump on a jet and visit them in less than a day. Just a half century ago, this type of lifestyle did not exist. In respect to our living space, it is rare for most of us to be in a totally natural environment, untouched by humans in any way. It is so rare that, to me, it seems like a sacred situation when I am lucky enough to be in such an environment. Yet, only a century ago, wildlife and wilderness were pervasive in the United States, and being surrounded by it was the norm rather than the exception. The job environment has changed just as quickly. Today there are fewer and fewer agricultural jobs. Being self-employed or owning a small business is becoming more and more difficult and competitive. Being dedicated to one company for your career is almost unheard of and even frowned upon. Less than a half century ago, this was not the case. Many families owned farms and were in touch with the mother earth; many other families owned local small businesses, such as hardware stores, pharmacies, local grocery stores, and restaurants. Today families are smaller. Typically, both spouses work, and often the emphasis is more on individuality rather than the family across the United States. Fewer people keep in touch with their childhood friends, despite having access to social media and telecommunications. Less than half a century ago, all of this was quite different. Families often stayed in one place for generations, and there was more of a sense of community. However, to survive and succeed, we must understand and acknowledge changes while they are happening and take the appropriate actions to adapt, stay healthy, and succeed.

Preparing for Change

The consequences of not adapting to change can be devastating; look no further than companies such as Sears & Roebuck, Kodak, and Pan Am Airlines. Once global giants, these organizations simply failed to adapt to change. While Pan Am no longer exists, Sears and Kodak are not far behind. Failure to plan and adapt to change led to the decline of these and many other once-prominent companies. People are the same. If we are not prepared and fail to adapt to change within our own environments, we too may end up having to downsize or even become unemployable.

So, how do you adapt to change? First, you must be aware of the changes happening around you. Next, you must find a way of measuring the effects of change and the effectiveness of alternative ways to adapt. For this purpose, I suggest that you manage your resources and your life much like the board of directors and upper management manages a corporation. A corporation has a strategic plan, research and development, marketing, finance and accounting, information processing, operations, and human resource departments; you too should have these departments in your personal life. Additionally, you may wish to have one or two close friends or colleagues who can act as your board to advise you.

Strategic Planning and Research and Development

As discussed in Chapter 3, a corporate strategic planning department is constantly thinking of new ideas and evaluating previously executed ideas with research and development. Likewise, each of us should be strategically planning our lives and testing new ideas to enhance them. If we like everything as it is today, we must look ahead and make sure the current situation will continue to be stable long enough to fulfill our needs.

For example, let's say you are a programmer and an expert in a coding language that is in high demand. Based on today's demand, you earn a salary that allows for a very comfortable lifestyle, as well as paying for your children's education and providing for your retirement years. However, if history shows that a coding language has a life cycle of about 10 years, you must be prepared for and adapt to this potential change. Accordingly, you may wish to research a promising new language and dedicate time to learning it.

The same process holds true for all jobs and careers. You never want to be caught off guard due to downsizing because your skill set is obsolete. In fact, one driving force to my completing this book is change in the healthcare profession itself. The current US healthcare model primarily focuses on treating people when they are sick, and it is becoming less economically viable. Additionally, the number of lives I can improve with the current model is limited to the time available in my schedule. However, by publishing a book, I can improve an unlimited number of lives each year. Additionally, this book will help people stay well and take the pressure off a healthcare model that is nearing economic collapse and failing to offer the level of care of years gone by. My time for change has come. Is it your time for change? You will know that only by staying aware of your professional environment, strategically planning ahead, and testing new ideas. You must constantly forecast the future of your career and prepare for change if you can see that your expectations will not be met.

Accounting and Finance

In addition to strategic planning and research and development, we should also adopt the concept of having our own internal accounting and finance department. To many people, this may seem like common sense and a very simple concept. However, many people choose to play the ostrich on this one and stick their heads in the sand until a crisis happens. This was most obvious during the 2008 financial crisis, when people over mortgaged and did not pay close enough attention to the effects of an increase in variable interest rates. Some people do have a personal accounting and finance department, but they might overlook key areas that could produce unexpected expenses— or even overlook opportunities that offer considerable revenue. For example, a friend of mine kept her house from being foreclosed on by offering it as a bed-and-breakfast alternative to vacationers for short-term stays; she also offered rooms for students as an alternative to dormitory life.

When considering accounting and finances, it is important to look at both the short term and long term. It is also important to have the knowledge of what you need for proper accounting and financial decision-making. Although it may seem daunting at first, it is not that complicated. Start by assessing your current financial position; this includes adding up all the cash you have available for spending and all other assets you could either turn into cash or take a loan against. After figuring your assets, you need to forecast projected income, by month, for the next year or so. This should include income from working, investments, and other sources. After projecting assets and income, forecast your monthly expenditures—including your cost of living, loan payments, and other outflows of cash. From this point, you can forecast cash and total net worth at any given point in the future. You can then use this information to determine the economic viability of any changes you may want to make in your life, including a new job, a new business venture, a vacation, a new toy, and so on. This type of forecasting is very important when it comes to new business ventures, which may absorb more cash and resources than they produce in the short run. In such cases, you will want to calculate how much net cash or assets are being spent each month. This is known as your *monthly burn rate*. When comparing your monthly burn rate to your available resources, you can predict how many months you can succeed given current finances. The idea is to forecast how long it will take to have a positive cash flow—and make sure you have enough resources to stay solvent until then. You can do this process for almost any endeavor, including your personal life. Forecasting in this way can help you plan your budget, manage expenses, and predict your future financial position and preparedness for any endeavor. I recommend that you do a forecast at least annually, and project your income and expenses over the next 5–10 years to ensure you can financially support your expectations and needs. If your needs will not be met, you must go back to strategic planning and research and development, and learn how to realistically adapt and make changes that will create a more favorable situation. Remember, our ancestors' ability to adapt to change is the only reason we are here today. Your own ability to adapt to change will ensure your survival and success.

Marketing and Sales

Most people do not think we need a marketing and sales function in our life. But, whether we realize it or not, we have customers no matter what we do. A marketing and sales department's job is to go out and find new customers, while cultivating current customers and making sure they are happy. We, too, must do the same. Perhaps we do not have to be as vigorous at sales and marketing as a professional. However, the function should not be overlooked in today's corporate jungle. Making people who use your services happy should always be on the forefront of your mind and part of your daily goals. Remember, your boss is your customer, your coworkers are your customers, and just about anyone you have contact with during the day can be perceived as your customer in one way or another. In fact, I recommend making a list of all the people you regularly interact with and define how they use your services. Next, write out creative ideas as to how you can make those people happy. It could be by saying *thank you* more often, smiling more often, being more personable, sharing stories, or offering tasteful tokens of appreciation (such as gift cards, etc.) on their birthdays. Although you may not have to look for new customers daily like a sales professional might, you should consider seeking out situations where you can make contacts who can help you grow, develop, and make any changes as needed. Looking for new customers (such as a new employer) may not be necessary every day, but considering today's ever rapidly changing environment, it is something that should always be in the back of your mind.

Information Technology

You may not need an entire information technology department, but it is important to define your informational needs and the technology that can provide for them. Less than

20 years ago, a person could be hugely successful without a cell phone. However, no matter what your job today, not owning a smart phone can greatly limit your ability to succeed. In addition to technology, you should consider the information that the technology supplies. For example, to perform your personal strategic planning and research and development, you may wish to subscribe to professional journals and publications that can help you to stay aware of growth and opportunities for your career, while avoiding threats in the marketplace. You also should consider what information you may need to properly fuel your hobbies, passions, and daily quiet time (see Chapter 6). Listening to podcasts, audio books, and online classes is an excellent and economical way of staying informed. This may or may not require a technological investment.

Operations

Personal operations can include everything from transportation to food and shelter. Basically, operations cover all the resources you need to operate successfully in both your personal and professional lives. If you like to ski, you need access to ski equipment and a mountain with snow. For your job, it might mean the ability to reasonably commute to and from your place of work. Our homes and vacation homes are also part of operations, as they help us to nurture ourselves during our daily quiet time and otherwise. Just as companies with slick operations departments can be economically and technologically efficient, properly defined personal operating equipment can do the same for our well-being and success. This might include nice clothes that you are proud to wear, a car you love to drive, a warm and comfortable home, etc. Make sure you have the best operations department practical to optimally support your personal and professional life. It may not be worth skimping on this department, as being supported by comfort will enhance your health and level of success.

Human Resources

Finally, defining your own human resources—that is, your state of health and skills—can be both challenging and rewarding. Hopefully many other chapters in this book have taught you how to do this and, correspondingly, how to preserve, nurture, grow, and develop your personal human resources. In particular, the most relevant information for doing this includes maintaining optimal health, healing, and longevity (Part 2); supporting and deepening your cognitive skills and the inner genius (Chapter 12); and identifying and expressing your passion (Chapter 13). Naturally, we all have limits that may restrict what we can do in our lives. Therefore, it is helpful to be aware of our own strengths and weaknesses and learn to adapt accordingly. At the end of the day, human resources are the basis for all we have. We need to utilize, maintain, and develop them wisely.

Resource Coordination

Just as corporations need to be aware of their strengths, weaknesses, marketplace opportunities, and marketplace threats, you must do the same. Just as corporations must have interdepartmental communication to best coordinate resources to meet their corporate missions, you too must coordinate resources. Therefore, I recommend that you have a mission statement that identifies who you are and defines your passions. As you define your passions, avoid falling prey to commercials and societal expectations. Review Chapter 13, know your passion, and use it to write your mission statement. It may take some time to write a mission statement, but it can give you a lifetime of purpose and drive. Review and practice the principles discussed in Part 2 on the Three Steps to Optimal Health, Healing, and Longevity. It is by staying in this state that you will maintain the clarity of mind needed to realize your mission. Regular maintenance of a PAD as discussed in Chapter 5 and expression of your passion (Chapter 13), will help you identify your inner emotions and what you really want in life. Use your PAD to devise a to-do list and then manage it according to your critical success factors and time management concepts (see Chapter 9). This will give you guidance and timelines for executing your mission. It will also assist you in forecasting your accounting and financial planning. As Chapter 10 describes, practicing good communication skills will help you in the sales and marketing of your mission; it will also help you identify and cultivate relationships that can open doors and present opportunities to help you manifest your mission's next level. By maintaining the state of optimal health, healing, and longevity, your intuition, cognitive skills, and inner genius will open up and give you insights on what you need for operations and what your true potential inner human resources are. This will also give you the confidence needed to take a leap of faith and make the necessary changes you need to stay healthy while excelling in the corporate jungle.

Summary

Adapting to change is as crucial a factor for surviving and excelling today as it was during the ice ages. Therefore, we should always be prepared for change and embrace it with confidence. We can prepare ourselves by being aware of our environment and strategically planning and steering our lives, much like a board of directors would steer a successful corporation. These factors will give your life structure, focused goals, deeper meaning, increased flexibility, stronger resilience to adversity, and more options. Overall, a better-planned life, with the ability to adapt to change, will fuel your heart and help you stay healthy and excel in all your endeavors, including the corporate environment so that it does not seem so much like a jungle.

CHAPTER 15

Skill 7—Maintaining a Positive and Winning Attitude

Maintaining a positive and winning attitude is another vital aspect to good health and success that is worthy of its own chapter. Many books and resources cover this subject. It is said that positivity breeds positivity. Many of the forms of daily quiet time discussed in Chapter 6 are great for maintaining a positive attitude. I was once told that it is just as easy to think everything will be fine than to worry about how it can go wrong. If you worry and things go well, you will have wasted internal resources in a fight-or-flight response that can adversely affect your health. Instead, if you maintain a positive attitude, you will receive the benefits that come from being in the state of optimal, health, healing, and longevity. Although it has been said that having a positive or negative disposition may be inherited, there is yet to be a gene associated with either. Therefore, it is safe to say that our parents and our upbringing condition us to be positive or negative. If you were lucky enough to be raised by parents who taught you to be an optimist and always think positively, you are very fortunate. However, if you were conditioned to be a pessimist, do not lose hope, as you can change. Maintaining a positive attitude is a skill. Like any other skill, it can be developed until you do it naturally without conscious effort. This chapter will describe the benefits of having a positive and winning attitude and what you can do to be more positive in your life; it will also offer some examples from my own life.

Benefits of a Positive Winning Attitude

Throughout time, much has been written on the benefits of having a positive attitude. Taoist monks maintain that, by simply smiling more, you can trigger internal happiness. This works because your CNS receives the message that you are happy by detecting that your facial muscles are smiling. A similar method is emphasized in Hindu beliefs, which teach us to avoid negative thoughts. By triggering the happy cascade and avoiding negativity, you will help maintain a positive attitude and keep yourself in the state of optimal health, healing, and longevity.

In addition to maintaining optimal health, there are two other reasons for maintaining a positive and winning attitude. One is *the law of attraction*, which basically says that, by maintaining a positive and winning attitude, you attract more reasons to have a positive and winning attitude. The other is based on psychology, which states that, when you maintain a positive and winning attitude, you will be psychologically healthier. This, in turn, allows you to maintain and exercise stronger cognitive skills while tapping into your inner genius and being creative throughout your day. This state allows you to better resolve most adversity and stay happy.

The law of attraction is based on the ancient Hindu principle of *karma*, which states that *for every action there is a reaction*. From a scientific viewpoint, this was echoed by physicist Sir Isaac Newton (1643–1727), who stated the same idea in his third law of motion. While Newton's law applied to physical objects, the concept of karma holds that the same law applies to metaphysical aspects of the universe, including human actions, words spoken, attitudes, emotions, and thoughts. Further, it states that you will attract SPECs (situations, people, events, and circumstances) that reflect the attitude or vibe that you project. So, according to karma, if you are grateful for all you have, you will attract SPECs that support being grateful for all you have. This can come in any form, including more money, a better job, an inheritance, satisfying relationships, new love, etc. Conversely, if you are always thinking of what you lack and project a vibe of desire, you will attract SPECs to reflect and support further desire. Again, this can come in any form, including a loss of a job, a car accident, a theft, being overlooked for a promotion, relationships ending, etc. Personally, I try to work with this concept as much as possible. In light of the fact that the attrition rate for acupuncturists is approximately 90%, I feel I am doing quite well at putting these principles into practice. However, it is not always easy to stay positive and be grateful. As mentioned above, it is a skill that needs to be developed and maintained. Depending on your background, this can be more challenging for some people than others.

How to Cultivate a Positive Attitude

The best way to start cultivating a positive attitude is to benchmark where you are currently. You can do this by keeping a log of how you feel throughout the day, writing down whether you feel positive or negative, the reason why, and the time you note the feeling. At the end of the day, you can figure out the percentage of time that you felt positive. See the following for an example of a log.

Time	Emotion: Positive or Negative	Reason
7:00 a.m.	Negative	Not a morning person
8:00	Negative	Traffic heavy during commute
9:00	Positive	Signed a profitable contract at work
10:00	Positive	Being productive; lots of positive feedback about the contract from boss and colleagues
11:00	Negative	The contract's paperwork is being held up in operations due to a formality
12:00 p.m.	Negative	Paperwork still being held up

Time	Emotion: Positive or Negative	Reason
1:00	Negative	Paperwork still being held up
2:00	Positive	Colleague shared a similar experience when all turned out fine
3:00	Positive	Being productive; working on other projects with more confidence than usual
4:00	Positive	Being productive; working on other projects with more confidence than usual
5:00	Positive	Feel like day was productive
6:00	Negative	Traffic in commute
7:00	Negative	Tired and worried about tomorrow
8:00	Negative	Tired and worried about tomorrow
9:00	Negative	Tired and worried about tomorrow
Summary	Of the 15 total hours:	

Time	Emotion: Positive or Negative	Reason
	• 9 were negative (60%) • 6 were positive (40%)	

Your objective should be to improve the percentage of the time each day and overall in your life that you feel positive. This can be done by identifying when your thoughts are negative and taking an action to turn them around. This may take some work, patience, and persistence to perfect. Following are some basic steps to help you do this.

After doing your attitude benchmarking, you can start by recognizing what makes you feel negative, then identify what you can do to turn things around and be more positive in the same situations. The chart below outlines alternative thoughts you might consciously consider to counter the negative thoughts. The long-term objective is to cognitively reeducate your subconscious reactions to automatically go to a positive place when events occur that may trigger a negative attitude. Correspondingly, it is helpful to reinforce positive feelings by acknowledging why you feel positive as such events happen. Therefore, it will be helpful to expand your log as follows.

Time	Emotion / Reason	Reaction
7:00 a.m.	Negative / Not a morning person	Simply smile. Look at something positive. Focus on the fact that you are alive, in good health, and have a job. Embrace

Time	Emotion / Reason	Reaction
		that you are not a morning person, and tell yourself that it's okay. Focus on the fact that you know you will feel better once you get going. Eventually, you may wish to do some introspection to uncover why you are not a morning person and address those issues.
8:00	Negative / Traffic heavy during commute	Simply smile. Look at something positive. Embrace the traffic, as it is probably there every day. Acknowledge that this is quiet time, time to yourself, time to do whatever you want while driving. You can listen to music, podcasts, audiobooks, talk on the phone, etc. Try to spend the time as valuably as possible and make the commute something you look forward to. If traffic is really bad, in the long run you may wish to investigate changing work hours or telecommuting some

Time	Emotion / Reason	Reaction
		days. You may even want to move or change jobs.
9:00	Positive / Contract was signed for profitable contract at work	Smile. Acknowledge that you are awesome at what you do, and that you know how to stay focused and close deals. Pat yourself on the back: you are a valuable asset to the company and, overall, you love what you do and are acknowledged for doing it well.
10:00	Positive / Being productive and a lot of positive feedback about the contract from boss and colleagues	Keep smiling. Be grateful for the acknowledgement above.
11:00	Negative / Paperwork for the contract is being held up in operations due to a formality	Keep smiling. Continue being grateful for the acknowledgement above. To put things in perspective, look at history and acknowledge that these things happen, and that 95% of the time they are resolved without much delay and 100% of the time they are resolved with some delay.

Time	Emotion / Reason	Reaction
12:00 p.m.	Negative / Paperwork still being held up	Smile. Continue as above.
1:00	Negative / Paperwork still being held up	Smile. Continue as above.
2:00	Positive / Colleague shared a similar experience when all turned out fine	Smile. Continue as above and be grateful for the support of colleagues.
3:00	Positive / Being productive working on other projects with more confidence than usual	Smile. Take time to acknowledge that you are awesome at what you do, and that you know how to stay focused and close deals. Pat yourself on the back: you are a valuable asset to the company and, overall, you love what you do and are acknowledged for doing it well.
4:00	Positive / Being productive working on other projects with more confidence than usual	Keep smiling. Be grateful for the acknowledgement above.
5:00	Positive / Feel like day was productive	Keep smiling. Be grateful for the acknowledgement above.

Time	Emotion / Reason	Reaction
6:00	Negative / Traffic in commute	Smile. Same as above in morning traffic.
7:00	Negative / Tired and worried about tomorrow	Smile. Take time to acknowledge that you are awesome at what you do, and that you know how to stay focused and close deals. Pat yourself on the back: you are a valuable asset to the company and, overall, you love what you do and are acknowledged for doing it well. Be grateful for all.
8:00	Negative / Tired and worried about tomorrow	Keep smiling. Be grateful for the acknowledgement above.
9:00	Negative / Tired and worried about tomorrow	Keep smiling. Be grateful for the acknowledgement above.

Notice that all the above *reactions* began with a smile. This is because the smile is so powerful and the easiest and most effective way of priming your mind to be positive.   This immediately opens up clarity and creativity to further assist with the next steps. I especially find it helpful to smile when I am in a neutral state—neither positive nor negative—as a smile always makes you feel more positive. Whenever you think about it, smile. Soon it will become the default expression on your face. This has been a big game changer in my life.

After expanding your log, use your written reactions as affirmations by saying them aloud to yourself to engrain them into your subconscious. For example, you can say "I am awesome at what I do" or "I am always smiling and happy." You may wish to do this throughout the day, before you go to sleep at night, and when you wake up in the morning. This will help you go to that positive place in your mind and automatically react in a positive way when challenging situations arise. Periodically, you can revisit your log to gauge your percentage of time being positive and negative and continuously increase the positivity.

Other ways of cultivating a positive attitude and discouraging a negative attitude are to revisit the forms of daily quiet time discussed in Chapter 6. You can cultivate a positive attitude during meditation, and ensure that your prayers always project a positive outcome. As I noted earlier, singing the Kumbaya camp song is a favorite method of mine. Staying in good shape with exercise, expressing passion, reading good books, watching inspirational movies, listening to uplifting music, and experiencing joy and laughter are all excellent ways to maintain a positive mental attitude. In addition, as I now describe, there are a few more underlying principles and helpful methods of maintaining a positive and winning attitude.

Methods to Maintain a Positive Winning Attitude

One of the most important aspects to maintaining a positive and winning attitude is to remember that *patience is a virtue*. You cannot always have what you want, when you want it. Therefore, you must have patience during challenging times and have confidence that things will change as long as you make efforts and project a positive and winning mental attitude. While you are waiting, you must look for signs that you are on the right path. As mentioned above, these signs will come in the form of SPECs, which simultaneously occur and give you confidence that you are on the right path to success. Pay attention to and follow up on these signs of encouragement, as they will give you the hope and inspiration to continue with the patience needed to see things through to a successful conclusion.

Many times, while on the path of success, you may wake up in a down mood. It may be difficult to have a positive and winning attitude during these moments. However, at these times, you must remember that Rome was not built overnight. During these times, you need to focus on doing anything that will make you feel better. It can be a cup of coffee, a walk, a shower, meditating, chanting, etc. Then, focus on another activity that will make you feel even better. I like to time myself with the stopwatch on my phone and see how long I can maintain happy and positive thoughts. As soon as I find myself thinking negatively, I check to see how long I lasted, reset the clock, and start again. Soon you will find happy and positive thoughts are the norm, and you will create a cascade of positive energy that will help you regain your positive attitude with focus, passion, and vigor.

Then there are the times when something seemingly horrible happens, and you just want to quit everything. This is where many give up. However, something bad can eventually bring many positive things into our life. In fact, you can be proactive in turning the situation around as follows. First, something horrible will give you feelings you definitely do not want to have; by identifying these feelings, you can firmly define the feelings you would rather have with conviction.

For example, let's say you are in a car accident, and your initial reaction is to feel like your life is falling apart. Then you realize that a better thought would be to celebrate that you are alive and without injury; you are grateful that you were blessed in the face of possible destruction. You keep reminding yourself of this with conviction. A feeling with conviction is a powerful concept.

Next, looking at things from the karmic idea of the law of attraction, you can strongly project those thoughts that will attract SPECs to help you manifest those feelings and support them in a physical sense. In the above example, you may realize life is short and finally take that vacation you desperately need and, upon your return, you feel like a new person. This in turn gives you the motivation to be more successful at work, resulting in that promotion you feared you would never get. Feelings with conviction can be just the catalyst you need to muster the energy and determination to make things happen.

To help identify your troublesome feelings and produce positive feelings with conviction, you can use a simple writing exercise. First, make two columns on a piece of lined paper. In the left column, list all the horrible feelings you are having. Then, in the right column, list the opposite feelings that you would rather have. Next, reread both. Then read the negative feelings one final time, tear the paper in half, and rip up and throw away the list with horrible feelings. Say goodbye to them. Next, take the list of positive feelings and start visualizing yourself manifesting them in your life. You can do that by using meditation or any other appropriate method above. Carry the list of positive feelings with you for as long as you need. Every time you feel down, smile and then read the list and imagine them manifesting in your life. It will not only make you feel better, but it will instill a positive and winning attitude necessary to preempt and actually create these feelings into your reality. Have fun with it and look for SPECs to give you confidence and reassurance that you are on the right path.

Another means of maintaining a positive and winning attitude in the face of adversity is to practice a set of principles I learned while at my first Deloitte & Touche training class. I had earned my way up from the bottom to the manager level in Deloitte's audit department, and then later to their consulting group. I must admit, it was one of the most competitive, demanding, and rewarding career experiences of my life. My Deloitte training and experience allowed me to work throughout the world and ultimately change careers and succeed at everything I did. However, I honestly believe that I could not have done it if they did not provide the training class on how to maintain a positive and winning attitude during my first month with the firm. Although I no longer remember his name, I can still remember the lecturer to this day and hear his voice in my head. I remember him saying that, to be a winner, you must remember that MISTAKES ARE OK. He further said that, if you could show him someone who never made a mistake, he would show you someone who never did much at all. However, he went on to say that mistakes are okay only if you learn from your mistakes and make sure you NEVER MAKE THE SAME MISTAKE TWICE. If you make the same mistake twice, it means you have a problem. But he went on to say that problems are okay because PROBLEMS ARE OPPORTUNITIES. Problems are opportunities to learn about yourself in order to discover why you made the same mistake twice. Knowing this, you can make the cognitive changes necessary to move forward confidently and successfully.

One unique thing about my experience in Deloitte's audit department was that, after each audit or project, we received a formal written evaluation. We received up to two of these evaluations each month. These evaluations went into your personnel file and determined your raise, your promotion, or even whether the company would retain you for another year. Further, this experience was unique because these evaluations were done by auditors. It always amazed me how they could give you an overall rating of very good to excellent, but if there was an area that needed improvement, they would seemingly spoil everything by writing a full page or even two about this one area. It was so disappointing to earn a great overall score, then get a long write up on your weakest performance area. Clearly, this experience overemphasized the negative aspects of our work and could have made us feel inadequate and want to give up. However, I was determined to be successful, and I looked at each negative write-up as a mistake. I would tell myself over and over, MISTAKES ARE OK, MISTAKES ARE OK.... JUST DO NOT MAKE THE SAME MISTAKE TWICE. Each time I made a contract with myself that I would never make the same mistake again. In addition, I always wrote a retort to my review, and I took the time to explain how much I had learned from the experience. As you might imagine, by stating how much I learned and following through by never repeating the same mistake twice, I created a nice personnel file for myself. Additionally, I disciplined myself to climb one of the most challenging learning curves regarding work and managerial skills that you can imagine.

These skills, of which perseverance was one, have helped me to achieve all that I have achieved today. Therefore, it feels most appropriate to close this book with this chapter, and at this point. Remember: mistakes are okay, as long as you do not make the same mistake twice. If you make the same mistake twice, it means you have a problem, which is simply an opportunity to learn about yourself and change. This process is rejuvenating and cultivates a positive attitude. Maintaining a positive and winning attitude is key to good health and success in the corporate jungle.

Summary

In conclusion, you cannot go wrong with a positive, winning attitude. Firstly, it will keep you out of the fight-or-flight state and help you maintain a state of optimal health, healing, and longevity. Secondly, in applying Newton's scientific law of cause and effect with the ancient metaphysical law of karma, a positive and winning attitude will attract SPECs to create physical manifestations to further support a positive and winning attitude. Thirdly, this attitude will help keep you psychologically healthy and prompt sharper cognitive and creative skills; these, in turn, will help you surmount adversity and resolve any issues in your path by encouraging the use of your inner genius.

Maintaining a positive and winning attitude is a skill, and like any other skill, it must be developed. I discussed some of the ways you can develop this skill above. The more you develop it, the easier and more natural it will be for you to present a positive, winning attitude in all aspects of life. In turn, this will create a cascade of events in your life that will simply give you more reasons to feel positive and always be a winner. This is when you will be most grateful and ready to teach others. Overall, it is my opinion that when you have a positive, winning attitude, you will in essence have everything, including your health, while excelling in the corporate jungle.

The Future of Evolution

As human beings, we have come a long way since the first hominins appeared on Earth some 7 million years ago. However, in relationship to our 4.5-billion-year-old Earth, we are still a young species and have much to learn as our culture and environment continue to change. *Both our applied human logic, which has allowed us to adapt to change, and our creativity, which has helped us develop skills and tools to assist in this adaptation, have been major contributing factors to our survival on Earth thus far. These same two factors will play an equally crucial role in our survival into the future.*

Corporate life has introduced many significant changes into how we live today. It has decreased most of the physical demands on our body that had previously existed since the ice ages. We no longer hunt and forage for our meals. Almost everything we need—from new clothes to a specific room temperature to cooked meals—can be achieved with the press of a button. We can communicate with the world from our desks, easily commute 60 miles or more for a job, and conceivably live our entire lives without ever experiencing a life-threatening event.

However, rising costs—for healthcare, sick pay, and disability pay—indicate that we have a lot to learn about our newly developed world. Nonetheless, the solution is simple. We just need to remember who we are as humans, how we are designed, and how to maximize our health and effectiveness. Following the best practices for maintaining optimal health, healing, and longevity (as outlined in Part 2, Chapters 4–8) is a logical place to start. Additionally, by developing and maintaining the necessary tools and skills for a successful corporate career (as outlined in Part 3, Chapters 9–15), we will exponentially increase our chances of excelling while staying healthy in our new environment. Finally, as corporate executives see the value in these best practices and make subtle changes in corporate environments to accommodate them, we will fully assure our success in conquering the challenges of corporate life—while reaping all its benefits.

Corporations have a lot of potential; I believe we are just scratching the surface of what they can achieve. Corporations have demonstrated the largest coordination of peaceful human efforts for a common focus in the history of humanity. Although not all corporate efforts and accomplishments have been for the betterment of mankind, *we must learn from our mistakes if we are to survive.* Given the potential magnitude and possible achievements that can be reached internationally through resource coordination and economies of scale, corporations could play a major role in world peace. Solid, focused corporate efforts have the potential of truly harmonizing the global human race. It is possible. The formula to get there is the same as what got us here and enabled human survival thus far. *We need to persevere, understand who we are, adapt to change, and continue to develop the tools and skills necessary to continue this adaptation as change occurs in the future.* If our efforts prove destructive, we must learn and change to be more constructive. This principal applies to corporations as much as to people. It is the only way. This is how we arrived at our current state, and it is the only way we will continue to survive and evolve further. *The day we stop learning from mistakes and stop adapting to change is the day we cease to exist.* Given my positive and winning attitude, I have great hopes for corporations and their role in evolution. We are learning, adapting, changing, and continuing that cycle.

Given our information age, I look forward to receiving feedback and hearing about your experiences as you implement the principles in this book. If you enjoyed the book and feel it would be helpful to others, please pass the word by leaving a positive review on the site where you purchased it. Meanwhile, I will continue to research, write, and facilitate change for the health and well-being of all.

Appendix A: Qi Gong Exercises

The following qi gong stretches are a simplification of the traditional Chinese Eight Treasures as taught to me by Master Dr. Hong Lui and further illustrated in his book Mastering Miracles. Note: All qi gong exercises should be done with care so as not to cause or aggravate injuries. If you suspect any injuries, always consult a healthcare professional before doing qi gong.

See my website www.DrJohnBarrett.com for future updates with videos demonstrating the following qi gong exercises.

1. Stretch for lower back, core muscles, chest, neck, head, and lungs.

With feet shoulder width apart, interlock hands and put them over head, extending the neck fully, looking up at your hands.

Next, stand on your toes and feel your lower back, core, and leg muscles engage.

Hold for 30 seconds, feeling your lungs open and enjoying increased circulation to your chest, neck, and head.

2. Stretches for upper back, shoulders, neck, arms, and wrists.

With feet shoulder width apart, cross arms on chest.

Swing top arm out to side, holding hand at 90º with fingers and thumb together.

Then raise the opposite arm and hold it as if you are pulling and imaginary bow string.

Keep your eyes on the extended hand while turning hips in opposite direction; extend chest out while bringing shoulder blades together in back.

Hold for 30 seconds, feeling the stretch of your upper back, shoulders, neck, arms, and wrists. Switch sides and repeat.

3. Stretches for the lower back, neck, chest, arms, wrists, core muscles, and leg muscles.

Push one hand down at right angle to center of body. Keep fingers and thumb together.

Push other hand up at right angle to center of body. Keep fingers and thumb together.

Stand on toes and hold for 30 seconds, feeling the stretch on the lower back, neck, chest, arms, and wrists. Feel the core muscles and leg muscles strengthen.

Come down off toes, switch hands to opposite directions, and repeat.

4. Stretches for ankles, knees, hips, lower back, shoulders, and neck.

Hold your hands on hips or 5" away.

Put your feet shoulder width apart, with knees slightly bent.

Rotate your body to left feeling ankles, knees, hips, lower back, shoulders, and neck fully stretch.

Hold for 30 seconds; turn the other way and repeat.

5. Stretches for ankles, knees, hips, lower back, shoulders, and neck.

Stand with feet straight, wider than shoulders, and hands on thighs.

Extend the left leg to a 45-degree angle, with the right knee slightly bent.

Rotate left shoulder to front; look over left shoulder at left foot.

Hold for 30 seconds, feeling hips, back, shoulders, and neck fully stretch.

Switch sides and repeat.

6. Stretches for lower back, hamstrings, calf muscles, arms, shoulders, and abdomen.

Put arms behind back with hands on kidneys, supporting the back. Lean back. Hold for 30 seconds, feeling the stretch of hip flexors, abdomen, and core muscles.

Slowly lean forward as far as you can go; hold for 30 seconds, feeling the stretch of the lower back, hamstrings, and calf muscles.

Next, extend upward and hold hands above head and lean back. Hold for 30 seconds, feeling arms, shoulders, and abdomen stretch.

Lean forward and allow hands to go as low as possible. Hold for 30 seconds, feeling lower back, hamstrings, and calf muscles stretch.

7. Exercise to build determination

Stand with feet at shoulder width and pointed straight, knees slightly bent and arms at side, holding fists with palm side up. Focus on a vertical object, such as a window frame, door frame, or tree.

Visualize the object as a challenge in your life—something you need to overcome, such as a bad habit or a dysfunctional relationship.

Stare determinedly at the object and then punch out, visualizing the challenge being overcome. Pull arm back, and punch with the other hand. You can punch as fast or as slow as you want.

This is more of a mental exercise than a physical one; it is designed to build determination and re-establish focus.

8. Exercise to wake up and loosen up (Part I)

Stand with feet straight and shoulder width.

Go onto toes imagining that someone is pulling you up by a string at the top of your head.

Hold, then imagine the string is cut and allow your heels to hit the ground. Repeat as desired.

Note: The jolt when the heels hit the ground can be therapeutic for the spine, but extreme caution should be used at first as to not aggravate the spine.

8. Exercise to wake up and loosen up (Part II)

Using the same starting position from Part I above, allow yourself to bounce up and down, on and off toes, without touching heels to the ground.

Allow the body to loosen up, shaking arms and shoulders as you do. Do repeatedly, imagining all negative energy falling off your body and returning to the Earth to be recycled into positive energy.